PEARSON   ALWAYS LEARNING

John Squires • Karen Wyrick

Notebook to accompany
Developmental Mathematics

Second Custom Edition for Liberty University Residential & Online

Taken from:
*MyMathLab® Notebook to accompany Developmental Mathematics:
Basic Mathematics, Introductory Algebra, and Intermediate Algebra,
Second Edition, by John Squires and Karen Wyrick*

D1472786

Pearson Learning Solutions, 330 Hudson Street, New York, New York 10013
A Pearson Education Company
www.pearsoned.com

Printed in the United States of America

2 3 4 5 6 7 8 9 10 V0UD 19 18 17 16 15

000200010271971740
000200010271979979

SR

Print: ISBN 10: 1-323-12923-5 / Print: ISBN 13: 978-1-323-12923-4
Media: ISBN 10: 1-323-16525-8 / Media: ISBN 13: 978-1-323-16525-6

Table of Contents

Name: _____   Date: _____

Instructor: _____   Section: _____

Notebook 2.1
Factors

A _____ is a number that is multiplied by another number.

Also, a factor is a whole number that _____ _____ into another number.

What are the factors of 6?

EXAMPLES 1 & 2 List all factors of 8.

List all factors of 24. Hint: Use factor pairs.

A _____ _____ is a number that divides exactly into two or more numbers. Can there be more than one?

What is the largest number that divides exactly into two or more numbers?

What are the steps finding the greatest common factor?
1. List all _____.
2. Identify the factors that are _____.
3. Choose the _____ of these _____ _____.

EXAMPLE 3 Find the greatest common factor, or GCF of 15 and 24.
Factors of 15:

Factors of 24:

Common factors:

Largest:

EXAMPLE 4 Find the greatest common factor, or GCF of 18 and 54.
Factors of 18:

Factors of 54:

Common factors:

Largest:

Rules for Divisibility:

A number is divisible by:	If:	Example:
2	It ends in …	
3	The sum of …	
5	It ends in …	
6	It is divisible by both …	
9	The sum of …	
10	It ends in …	

EXAMPLE 5 Find the GCF of 132 and 198.

Factors of 132:

Factors of 198:

Common factors:

Largest:

What does "to factor" mean?

EXAMPLE 6 List three ways to factor 18.

CONCEPT CHECK: What is a factor?

GUIDED EXAMPLES:

1. Is 1695 divisible by 2? 3? 5? 9? 10?

2. Find the GCF of 12 and 16.

3. Find the GCF of 24 and 56.

4. List as least 2 ways to factor 36.

Notebook 2.2
Prime Factorization

Factor (noun) – a number that is being _____.
Factor (verb) – to write as a _____.

EXAMPLE 1 a. Find all factors of 36.   b. Factor 36 several ways.

A _____ _____ is a whole number greater than 1 that has exactly two factors, the number itself and 1.

Is 0 prime?   Is 1 prime?

Prime Numbers:

Whole Number	Factors	Prime??
2		
3		
4		
5		
6		
7		
8		
9		

Write down the first 15 prime numbers:

_____ _____ are whole numbers greater than 1 that are not prime.

Is 0 composite?   Is 1 composite?

True/False: Every number is either prime or composite.

EXAMPLE 2 Identify each whole number as prime, composite, or neither.
    2, 8, 1, 13, 22, 55, 29, 37, 99

The _____ _____ of any whole number is the factored form in which all factors are prime numbers.

What are the steps for finding the prime factorization?

1. Write the number as a _____ of _____.

2. Check to see if each of these factors is _____.
   If so, _____; if not, write it as a _____.

3. Continue to do this until all factors are _____.

4. Write the prime factorization as a product of all the _____

   _____ _____.

EXAMPLE 3 Find the prime factorization of 24.

EXAMPLE 4 Find the prime factorization of 60.

Note: If factors are listed from smallest to largest, every composite number's prime factorization can be written in _____.

CONCEPT CHECK: How many factors does a prime number have?

GUIDED EXAMPLES:
1. Identify as prime, composite, or neither. 55 _____ 17 _____

2. Find the prime factorization of 35.

3. Find the prime factorization of 48.

4. Find the prime factorization of 28.

Name: _____   Date: _____

Instructor: _____   Section: _____

Notebook 2.3
Understanding Fractions

What is the difference between whole numbers and fractions?
Give examples of each.

What are numbers that represent the parts of a whole?

EXAMPLE 1 A pizza has 8 slices. Sam ate 3 of the 8 slices for lunch.

The top number of a fraction is called the _____.

The bottom number of a fraction is called the _____.

Which one indicates the number of equal parts being considered?

Which one indicates the number of parts in the whole?

EXAMPLE 2 Write a fraction that best represents the shaded part.

a.

b.

c.

What kind of fraction has the numerator less than the denominator?
Proper or improper??
A proper fraction has a value _____ _____ 1.

Write some examples of proper fractions:

What kind of fraction has the numerator greater than or equal to
the denominator? Proper or improper??

An improper fraction has a value _____.

Write some examples of improper fractions:

5

Note: Any whole number greater than or equal to 1 can be written as an
_____ _____ with the number in the numerator and a
_____ in the denominator.

EXAMPLES 3–7 Identify each fraction as proper or improper.

$$\frac{4}{9}$$

$$\frac{11}{4}$$

$$\frac{7}{6}$$

$$\frac{3}{3}$$

$$\frac{0}{5}$$

Four Basic Facts about Fractions:
1. Any non-zero number divided by itself is _____.
   Ex.
2. Any number divided by 1 is _____.
   Ex.
3. Zero divided by any non-zero number is _____.
   Ex.
4. Division by 0 is _____.
   Ex.

CONCEPT CHECK: Division by zero is _____.

GUIDED EXAMPLES:
1. Write a fraction that represents the shaded part.

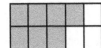

2. Identify $\frac{0}{7}$ as proper or improper

3. Identify $\frac{4}{4}$ as proper or improper.

4. Simplify $\frac{11}{0}$.

6

Notebook 2.4
Simplifying Fractions—GCF and Factors Method

Every fraction can be written in many ways.
Write several different ways to represent one-half.

What are equivalent fractions?

A fraction is said to be in _____ _____
if there is _____ _____ _____ other than 1
that divides exactly into the _____ and _____.

What are the steps to simplify a fraction using the GCF method?
1. Find the _____ of the numerator and denominator.

2. Divide the _____ and _____ by the _____.

True/False: Dividing the numerator and the denominator by
the same non-zero number does not change the value of a fraction.

EXAMPLE 1 Write in simplest form using the GCF method. $\dfrac{9}{15}$

Find the GCF:

Divide numerator and denominator by GCF:

EXAMPLE 2 Write in simplest form using the GCF method. $\dfrac{72}{96}$

Find the GCF:

Divide the numerator and denominator by GCF:

If you are having a hard time finding the GCF, use any common factor.

What are the steps for simplifying fractions using the factors method?
1. Find any factor that is _____.

2. Divide the numerator and denominator by _____.

3. Repeat this until there are _____.

7

EXAMPLE 3 Write in simplest form using the factors method. $\dfrac{20}{32}$

EXAMPLE 4 Write in simplest form using the factors method. $\dfrac{72}{96}$

CONCEPT CHECK: To simplify $\dfrac{10}{20}$ using the GCF method, what number will be divided into the numerator and denominator?

GUIDED EXAMPLES:

Write in simplest form using the GCF method.

1. $\dfrac{12}{16}$

2. $\dfrac{75}{125}$

Write in simplest form using the factors method.

3. $\dfrac{30}{75}$

4. $\dfrac{24}{54}$

Notebook 2.5
Simplifying Fractions—Prime Factors Method

We can use prime factorizations to write a fraction in simplest form.

What are the steps for simplifying fractions using the
Prime Factors Method?
1. Write the numerator as a _____.
2. Write the denominator as a _____.
3. Divide by _____ in the numerator
   and denominator.
4. Multiply the _____ _____ to get simplest form.

Note: What results when you divide the numerator and denominator by the
same non-zero number?

EXAMPLE 1 Write in simplest form using the prime factors method. $\dfrac{24}{36}$

Write numerator as a product of primes:

Write denominator as a product of primes:

Divide numerator and denominator
by common factors:

Multiply the remaining factors:

EXAMPLE 2 Write in simplest form using the prime factors method. $\dfrac{84}{91}$

Write numerator as a product of primes:

Write denominator as a product of primes:

Divide numerator and denominator
by common factors:

Multiply the remaining factors:

EXAMPLE 3 Write in simplest form using the prime factors method. $\dfrac{39}{195}$

Write numerator as a product of primes:

Write denominator as a product of primes:

Divide numerator and denominator by common factors:

Multiply the remaining factors:

CONCEPT CHECK: When dividing the numerator and denominator of a fraction by the same non-zero number, what happens to the value of the original fraction?

GUIDED EXAMPLES:

1. Write in simplest form using the prime factors method. $\dfrac{25}{35}$

2. Write in simplest form using the prime factors method. $\dfrac{84}{90}$

3. Write in simplest form using the prime factors method. $\dfrac{42}{126}$

10

Notebook 2.6
Multiplying Fractions

How do you find $\dfrac{1}{2}$ of $\dfrac{2}{3}$?

Show this.

What are the steps for multiplying fractions?
1.
2.
3.

EXAMPLE 1 Multiply. Write your answer in simplest form. $\dfrac{4}{7}\cdot\dfrac{3}{5}$

Multiply numerators.

Multiply denominators.

Simplify.

EXAMPLE 2 Multiply. Write your answer in simplest form. $\dfrac{7}{10}\cdot\dfrac{5}{8}$

Multiply numerators.

Multiply denominators.

Simplify.

What are the steps for multiplying fractions by simplifying first?
1.
2.
3.

EXAMPLE 3 Multiply by simplifying first. $\dfrac{7}{10}\cdot\dfrac{5}{8}$

Write as one fraction.

Divide by common factors.

Multiply the remaining factors.

EXAMPLE 4 Multiply by simplifying first. $\dfrac{4}{15} \cdot \dfrac{9}{16}$

EXAMPLE 5 Multiply by simplifying first. $3 \cdot \dfrac{2}{9}$

EXAMPLE 6 Elizabeth bought a sandwich and ate half of it. She gave her brother one-half of what was left. How much of the sandwich did her brother get?
Understand the problem.

Create a plan.

Find the answer.

Check the answer.

EXAMPLE 7 Multiply by simplifying first. $\dfrac{2}{8} \cdot \dfrac{5}{15}$

CONCEPT CHECK: You multiplied fractions to get $\dfrac{33}{48}$. What will your final answer be?

GUIDED EXAMPLES:

1. Multiply $\dfrac{2}{3} \cdot \dfrac{4}{9}$. Write your answer in simplest form.

2. Multiply $\dfrac{3}{10} \cdot \dfrac{5}{24}$ by simplifying first.

3. Multiply $\dfrac{2}{7} \cdot \dfrac{21}{50}$ by simplifying first.

4. Multiply $\dfrac{3}{8} \cdot 2$ by simplifying first.

12

Notebook 2.7
Dividing Fractions

How do you know if two numbers are reciprocals?

How do you find the reciprocal of a fraction?

How do you find the reciprocal of a whole number?

EXAMPLES 1 & 2 Find the reciprocals of the following numbers.

$\dfrac{3}{4}$

5

What is the reciprocal of 0?

What happens when you divide a number by 2 and multiply the same

number by $\dfrac{1}{2}$?

Rule: Dividing by a fraction is the same as _____.

What are the steps for dividing fractions?
1.
2.
3.
4.

EXAMPLE 3 Divide. Write your answer in simplest form. $\dfrac{3}{5} \div \dfrac{1}{2}$

Invert the second fraction.

Multiply by the first fraction.

Divide by common factors.

Multiply the remaining factors.

13

EXAMPLES 4 & 5 Divide. Write your answers in simplest form.

$$\frac{4}{5} \div \frac{3}{8}$$

$$\frac{6}{7} \div \frac{3}{2}$$

.

EXAMPLES 6 & 7 Divide. Write your answers in simplest form.

$$12 \div \frac{2}{3}$$

$$\frac{6}{7} \div 9$$

CONCEPT CHECK: How would you rewrite $\frac{3}{8} \div \frac{4}{9}$ as a multiplication

problem?

GUIDED EXAMPLES:
Divide each of the following. Write your answer in simplest form.

1. $\frac{2}{3} \div \frac{4}{5}$

2. $\frac{4}{7} \div \frac{8}{11}$

3. $\frac{9}{10} \div 6$

4. $\frac{5}{12} \div \frac{15}{16}$

14

Notebook 3.3
Finding the LCM—Prime Factor Method

What is prime factorization of any whole number?

EXAMPLES 1 & 2
      Find the prime factorization of 12.

      Find the prime factorization of 42.

What are the steps for finding the LCM of two numbers using the prime factor method?
1.
2.
3.
4.

EXAMPLE 3 Find the LCM of 12 and 42 using the Prime Factor Method.
Prime factorization of 12:

Prime factorization of 42:

LCM:

EXAMPLE 4 Find the LCM of 8 and 30.
Prime factorization of 8:

Prime factorization of 30:

Write the prime factorizations
putting the common factors below
each other:

Write down the prime factor from
each column:

Multiply the lists of primes to get LCM:

15

EXAMPLE 5 Find the LCM of 18 and 24.

EXAMPLE 6 Find the LCM of 13 and 19.

CONCEPT CHECK: Write the prime factorization of 24.

GUIDED EXAMPLES:
Find the LCM of each pair of numbers using the prime factor method.
1. 15 and 21

2. 20 and 45

3. 72 and 84

16

Notebook 3.4
Writing Fractions with an LCD

Things to consider when finding the LCM:
1. If one number divides exactly into the other, then the LCM is …

Give an example:

2. If the numbers have no common factor other than 1, then the LCM is …

Give an example:

3. If the two numbers have a common factor other than 1, then …

Give an example:

What are some methods that can be used to find the LCM?

What is the difference between LCM and LCD?

What is the least common denominator (LCD)?

EXAMPLES 1 & 2
      Find the LCM of 4 and 12.

      Find the LCD of $\frac{3}{4}$ and $\frac{5}{12}$.

True/False The same process is used to find both the LCD and the LCM.

Fractions are _____ _____ if they represent the same value.

Name some other fractions that represent $\frac{1}{6}$.

17

What are the steps for writing an equivalent fraction?

EXAMPLE 3 Write a fraction equivalent to $\dfrac{1}{6}$ using a denominator of 12.

List the steps for writing fractions with an LCD.
1.

2.

3.

EXAMPLE 4 Rewrite $\dfrac{1}{6}$ and $\dfrac{7}{9}$ using the LCD as the denominator.

EXAMPLE 5 Rewrite $\dfrac{4}{15}$ and $\dfrac{5}{6}$ using the LCD as the denominator.

CONCEPT CHECK:

After finding the LCD of $\dfrac{1}{6}$ and $\dfrac{2}{7}$, what number will we multiply 6 by to get an equivalent fraction?

GUIDED EXAMPLES:

1. Rewrite $\dfrac{5}{8}$ using 24 as the denominator.

2. Rewrite $\dfrac{11}{12}$ and $\dfrac{7}{18}$ using the LCD as the denominator.

3. Rewrite $\dfrac{2}{3}$ and $\dfrac{3}{7}$ using the LCD as the denominator.

18

Notebook 3.5
Adding and Subtracting Like Fractions

Fractions with the same, or common, denominator are called
_____ _____.

What are unlike fractions?

EXAMPLES 1 & 2

$\dfrac{1}{8}$, $\dfrac{3}{8}$, and $\dfrac{7}{8}$ are _____ fractions.

$\dfrac{3}{7}$ and $\dfrac{3}{5}$ are _____ fractions.

Write the steps for adding like fractions:
1.
2.
3.

EXAMPLES 3 & 4 Add the following like fractions. Simplify if possible. .

$\dfrac{2}{5} + \dfrac{1}{5}$

$\dfrac{3}{10} + \dfrac{3}{10}$

Write the steps for subtracting like fractions:

1.
2.
3.

EXAMPLES 5 & 6 Subtract the following like fractions. Simplify if possible.

$\dfrac{6}{7} - \dfrac{2}{7}$

$\dfrac{11}{14} - \dfrac{5}{14}$

OTHER NOTES

19

EXAMPLES 7 & 8 Add or subtract the following like fractions. Simplify if possible.

$$\frac{4}{11}+\frac{3}{11}+\frac{5}{11}$$

$$\frac{7}{8}-\frac{3}{8}$$

EXAMPLE 9 Shauna ate $\frac{1}{8}$ of a pizza and Kenzi ate $\frac{3}{8}$ of the same pizza.

Together how much of the pizza did the two girls eat?

Understand the problem.

Create a plan.

Find the answer.

Check the answer.

CONCEPT CHECK: Danette walked to the store. First she walked down a street that is $\frac{2}{10}$ of a mile long, and then down another street that is $\frac{5}{10}$ of a mile long. Create a plan to show how far she walked to the store.

GUIDED EXAMPLES:

1. Subtract the like fractions $\frac{7}{10}-\frac{4}{10}$. Simplify if possible.

2. Add the like fractions $\frac{2}{15}+\frac{8}{15}$. Simplify if possible.

3. Subtract the like fractions $\frac{7}{9}-\frac{4}{9}$. Simplify if possible.

4. Add the like fractions $\frac{7}{12}+\frac{7}{12}+\frac{1}{12}$. Simplify if possible.

20

Notebook 3.6
Adding and Subtracting Unlike Fractions

What is the first thing you must do to add or subtract unlike fractions?

Caution!! You must have a _____ _____
when _____ or _____ fractions.

Write down the steps for adding and subtracting unlike fractions:
1.

2.

3.

4.

5.

EXAMPLE 1 Add $\frac{3}{4} + \frac{1}{6}$. Simplify if possible.
Find the LCD.

Rewrite each fraction with
the LCD as the denominator.

Add the numerators.
Keep the denominator.
Simplify if possible.

EXAMPLE 2 Add $\frac{3}{8} + \frac{2}{5}$. Simplify if possible.

EXAMPLE 3 Subtract $\frac{5}{6} - \frac{1}{3}$. Simplify if possible.

EXAMPLE 4 Subtract $\dfrac{7}{10} - \dfrac{4}{15}$. Simplify if possible.

EXAMPLE 5 Paul ate $\dfrac{3}{8}$ of an apple pie. His brother Jeff ate $\dfrac{1}{4}$ of the same pie.

How much more pie did Paul eat than Jeff?

Understand the problem

Create a plan

Find the answer

Check the answer

CONCEPT CHECK:

For the problem $\dfrac{5}{9} - \dfrac{1}{3}$, what is the first step?

GUIDED EXAMPLES:

1. Add $\dfrac{3}{7} + \dfrac{2}{5}$. Simplify if possible.

2. Add $\dfrac{1}{14} + \dfrac{3}{7}$. Simplify if possible.

3. Subtract $\dfrac{4}{9} - \dfrac{1}{12}$. Simplify if possible.

4. Subtract $\dfrac{14}{15} - \dfrac{3}{5}$. Simplify if possible.

Notebook 3.7
Order of Operations and Fractions

Recall: When there is more than one operation involved, use the Order of Operations so that you will know the order in which to perform the operations.

Write down the steps for using the order of operations:
P:

E:

MD:

AS:

Remember, certain symbols can act like parentheses. What are they?

EXAMPLE 1 Simplify by using the order of operations. $\left(\dfrac{1}{3}-\dfrac{1}{6}\right)+\dfrac{1}{2}$

P:

E:

MD:

AS:

Simplify:

EXAMPLE 2 Simplify. $\left(\dfrac{2}{5}+\dfrac{1}{5}\right)^2 \div \dfrac{3}{10}$

P:

E:

MD:

AS:

Simplify:

EXAMPLE 3 Simplify. $\dfrac{1}{4} \div \dfrac{3}{2} + \dfrac{1}{2} \cdot \dfrac{1}{3}$

P:

E:

MD:

AS:

Simplify:

EXAMPLE 4 Simplify by using the order of operations.

$\left(\dfrac{3}{4}\right)\left(\dfrac{1}{2} - \dfrac{1}{4}\right)^2 + \dfrac{2}{5} \cdot \dfrac{1}{2}$

P:

E:

MD:

AS:

Simplify:

CONCEPT CHECK:

Given the problem, $\dfrac{1}{2}\left(\dfrac{3}{4} - \dfrac{1}{8}\right) + \left(\dfrac{1}{5}\right)^2$ which operation is performed first?

GUIDED EXAMPLES:

Simplify each of the following.

1. $\dfrac{3}{5} + \dfrac{1}{4} \cdot \dfrac{2}{3} - \dfrac{1}{10}$

2. $\dfrac{2}{3} \div \left(\dfrac{5}{8} + \dfrac{1}{2}\right) - \dfrac{1}{9}$

3. $\dfrac{5}{6} \cdot \dfrac{1}{2} + \left(\dfrac{2}{3} \div \dfrac{4}{9}\right)^2$

24

Name: _____   Date: _____

Instructor: _____   Section: _____

Notebook 5.4
Adding and Subtracting Decimals

How is adding and subtracting decimals similar to adding and subtracting whole numbers and like fractions?

EXAMPLE 1 Jennifer spent $2.97 for a meal and $1.19 for dessert, including tax. How much did she spend in total?

What is the procedure for adding and subtracting decimals?
1. Write the numbers _____, …
2. Write all decimals with …
3. Add or subtract, starting …
4. Place the decimal point …

EXAMPLES 2 & 3 Add. Check by estimating.
$3.27 + 15.2$ $4 + 12.3 + 0.571$

EXAMPLES 4 & 5 Find the difference. Check by estimating.
$13.24 - 7$ $21.5 - 16.43$

What is the perimeter of a triangle?

How do you find the perimeter of a triangle?

EXAMPLE 6 Find the perimeter of the triangle.

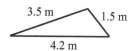
3.5 m   1.5 m
    4.2 m

EXAMPLE 7 At Sandee's Malt Shop, a hamburger costs $3.95, a hot dog costs $2.49, French fries cost $1.59, and onion rings cost $1.89. How much more does a hamburger with French fries cost than a hot dog with onion rings?
Understand the problem

Create a plan

Find the answer

Check your answer

CONCEPT CHECK:
A triangle has sides of length 10.9 in., 8.2 in., and 8.1 in. What is the proper expression for finding its perimeter?

GUIDED EXAMPLES:
1. Add. $20.52 + 6.9 + 13.8$

2. Add. $9 + 6.501 + 43.2$

3. Subtract. $246.72 - 98.264$

4. Subtract. $62.2 - 51.98$

Notebook 5.5
Multiplying Decimals

Show why multiplying $\frac{3}{10}$ and $\frac{2}{10}$ is the same as multiplying 0.2 and 0.3.

Write the steps for multiplying decimals.

1.

2.

3.

EXAMPLES 1 & 2 Multiply.

3.45(6.1) 0.152×0.23

EXAMPLES 3 & 4 Multiply.

3.2×0.008 4 (2.5)

What is the procedure for multiplying a decimal by a power of 10?

What do you do if the number of zeros is more than the number
of original decimal places?

EXAMPLE 5 Multiply.

5.793×100

EXAMPLES 6 & 7 Multiply.

79.251 × 10   42.8 × 1000

EXAMPLE 8 Ian's new car travels 25.6 miles for each gallon of gas. How many miles can he travel on a full tank, which contains 12 gallons of gas?

Understand the problem

Create a plan

Find the answer

Check your answer

CONCEPT CHECK:

Nataliya jogs seven days a week along a running path that is 2.9 miles long. Her goal is to jog 20 miles a week. Does she achieve her goal by jogging this path every day?

GUIDED EXAMPLES:

1. Multiply. 1.5 × 3.1

2. Multiply. 0.035 × 0.08

3. Multiply. 68.157 × 100

4. Multiply. 9.63 × 10,000

Notebook 5.6
Dividing Decimals

What is the number being divided?
What is the number the dividend is being divided by?
What is the answer to a division problem?

Label each part of a division problem in three different ways:

What is the rule for dividing a decimal by a whole number?

EXAMPLE 1 Divide. $6.3 \div 3$

EXAMPLE 2 Simon, Penny, Ashley, and James went out to eat. The total bill was $36.24. If they split the bill evenly, how much did each person pay?
Understand the problem

Create a plan

Find the answer

Check the answer

EXAMPLE 3 Divide. $6.7 \div 10$

Write the rule for dividing a decimal by a power of 10.

What do you do if the number of zeros is more than the number of whole number places?

EXAMPLE 4 Divide. $2.9 \div 1000$

What happens when we divide 3.8 by 4?
When working with decimals, there are no _____.

What are the three possibilities when dividing decimals?
1.

2.

3.

EXAMPLE 5 Divide 6.1 by 3.

Write the steps for dividing a decimal by a decimal.
1.

2.

3.

4.

EXAMPLE 6 Divide. $0.0612 \div 0.12$

EXAMPLE 7 Divide. Round to the nearest hundredth. $1.219 \div 0.3$

CONCEPT CHECK:
In the problem $19.21\overline{)24.567}$, what does the dividend become after the divisor has been changed to a whole number?

GUIDED EXAMPLES:
1. Divide. $8.64 \div 4$

2. Divide. $245.967 \div 1000$

3. Divide. Round to the nearest tenth. $1.4 \div 0.6$

4. Divide. $5.564 \div 4.28$

30

Notebook 5.7
Order of Operations and Decimals

Write down the steps for using the order of operations:
P:

E:

MD:

AS:

Remember, certain symbols can act like parentheses. What are they?

What are the two memory tips for remembering the order of operations?

EXAMPLES 1 & 2 Simplify.

$3.6 + (0.2 + 0.3)^2$

  P:

  E:

  MD:

  AS:

$(12.6 - 11.4)^2 \div (0.2)(3)$

  P:

  E:

  MD:

  AS:

EXAMPLES 3 & 4 Simplify.

$10.5 - 3.2 + 7.2 \div 3.6$

   P:

   E:

   MD:

   AS:

$10 \div 5(0.1)^2$

   P:

   E:

   MD:

   AS:

Note: A fraction bar can also act like _____.

EXAMPLE 5 Simplify. $\dfrac{10.1 + 2.1(3)}{5.05 + 3.15}$

P:

E:

MD:

AS:

CONCEPT CHECK:
What is the second calculation involved in evaluating $19.12 - 9.6 \div 1.2 \times 1.5$?

GUIDED EXAMPLES:
1. Simplify. $7.1 - (0.6)(0.5 \div 1.25)^2$

2. Simplify. $12.6 \div 3 + (1.8 + 0.4)^2$

3. Simplify. $2.1 + 8.4 \times 3.12 - 1.37$

32

Name: _____   Date: _____

Instructor: _____   Section: _____

Notebook 6.1
Ratios

What is a ratio?

What are the different ways in which a ratio can be written?
Give examples.

EXAMPLE 1 A gallon of lemonade is made by mixing 2 cups of lemon juice with 14 cups of water. Write the ratio of lemon juice to water in a gallon of lemonade.

What is the rule for writing ratios as fractions?
    The quantity appearing first is …

    The quantity appearing second is …

EXAMPLE 2 Write 5 hours to 7 hours as a ratio. Use all three ways.

Do we need to include the units in ratios? _____ Why or why not?

EXAMPLES 3 & 4 Write the following ratios as fractions in simplest form.

    5 inches to 11 inches

    4 ounces: 32 ounces

33

EXAMPLES 5 & 6 Write the following ratios as fractions in simplest form.
$1.23 to $3.75

Joseph lost $5\frac{1}{2}$ pounds, while his friend Demarcus lost $3\frac{1}{4}$ pounds.

Find the ratio of the weight that Joseph lost to the weight that Demarcus lost.

EXAMPLE 7 A cake recipe requires $2\frac{1}{2}$ cups of flour and $1\frac{3}{4}$ cups of sugar.

Write the ratio of the amount of flour to the amount of sugar as a fraction in the simplest form.

Understand the problem

Create a plan

Find the answer

Check the answer

CONCEPT CHECK: True/False The quantity appearing second appears in the numerator.

GUIDED EXAMPLES:
Write each ratio as a fraction in simplest form.
1. 11 inches to 9 inches

2. $1\frac{1}{2}$ hours to $3\frac{1}{2}$ hours

3. $3\frac{3}{4}$ gallons to $4\frac{1}{2}$ gallons

4. Mark's truck can tow 2.5 tons and Kyle's truck can tow 5.0 tons.
   Find the ratio of the towing capacity of Mark's truck to the towing capacity of Kyle's truck.

34

Notebook 6.2
Rates

What is a rate?

What are two common examples of rates?

What is the rule for writing rates as fractions?
     The quantity appearing first is …

     The quantity appearing second is …

Do we need to include the units in rates? _____ Why or why not?

EXAMPLE 1 Write the rate as a fraction in simplest form.
     240 miles per 10 gallons

EXAMPLE 2 Write the rate as a fraction in simplest form.
     18 tomatoes for 4 pots of stew

EXAMPLES 3 & 4 Write the following ratios as fractions in simplest form.

     20 door prizes for 110 people

     $250 for 20 hours

What is a unit rate?

What is the difference between a rate and a unit rate?

EXAMPLE 5 Find the unit rate.

A 6-pack of juice bottles costs $3.00. Find the unit rate of cost per 1 bottle.

Note: To find a rate, write the rate as ...

To find a unit rate, write the rate as ...

What is the procedure for finding the better buy?

EXAMPLE 6 Which of the following is a better buy?
A 12-ounce box of Antonio's Macaroni costs $2.08.

A 15-ounce box of Sally's Macaroni costs $3.05.

Solution: Find the cost per ounce for each box:

What is the cost per ounce for a 12-ounce box?

What is the cost per ounce for a 15-ounce box?

Which one is the better buy?

CONCEPT CHECK: True/False The best buy has the highest unit cost.

GUIDED EXAMPLES:
Write the rate as a fraction in simplest form.
1. 15 departments for 10 salespeople

2. $210 for 28 pizzas

3. Find the unit rate of miles per gallon. 118 miles for 5 gallons

4. Murphy's Crunch cereal comes in a 16-ounce box for $3.20 and Dawn's Nuggets cereal comes in a 25-ounce box for $6.00. Which is the better buy?

Notebook 6.3
Proportions

What is an equation?

What is a proportion?

EXAMPLES 1 & 2 For each example, write as a proportion.
3 is to 6 as 12 is to 24

Caleb paid $60 for 4 tickets and Beth paid $90 for 6 tickets.

CAUTION!! Is consistency important when setting up a proportion?
What does that mean?

What is the procedure for determining if a statement is a proportion?

If the cross products are equal, then the statement is …
If the cross products are not equal, then the statement is …

EXAMPLES 3 & 4 Determine if the statement is a proportion.

$$\frac{6}{21} = \frac{10}{35}$$

$$\frac{2}{3.1} = \frac{3}{3.7}$$

If we know three of the four numbers in a proportion, $\frac{a}{b} = \frac{c}{d}$, such that $b \neq 0$

and $d \neq 0$, can we find the fourth number?
Does it matter which one is missing?

EXAMPLE 5 Find the missing number in the proportion.

$$\frac{3}{9} = \frac{4}{?}$$

Write the steps for finding missing number in a proportion:
1. Calculate the _____ and set them

   _____.

2. Divide both sides of the equation by …

EXAMPLE 6 Find the missing number in the proportion.

$$\frac{5}{6} = \frac{n}{12}$$

Check:

EXAMPLE 7 The proper dosage of a children's medicine is 40mg for every 50 pounds. How much medicine do you give a child weighing 75 pounds?
Understand the problem

Create a plan

Find the answer

Check the answer

CONCEPT CHECK: What symbol does ALL equations contain?

GUIDED EXAMPLES:
1. Write the following as a proportion.

   7 is to 12 as 14 is to 24

2. Determine if the statement is a proportion.

   $$\frac{3.6}{4.8} \stackrel{?}{=} \frac{2.4}{3.2}.$$

3. Find the missing number In the proportion.

   $$\frac{5}{7} = \frac{n}{28}$$

4. You can drive 200 miles on 8.5 gallons of gas. How much gas will it take to drive 600 miles?

Notebook 6.4
Percent Notation

What does percent mean?

What are some examples of percents?

How do you write a percent as a fraction?

EXAMPLES 1–3 Write each percent as a fraction in simplest form.

47%

14%

136%

When is it easy to convert fractions to percents?

EXAMPLES 4 & 5 Write each fraction as a percent.

$$\frac{7}{100}$$

$$\frac{61}{100}$$

EXAMPLES 6–8 Answer the following questions involving percents. Penny answered 87 out of 100 problems correctly on her math test. What percent of the problems did she answer correctly?

68 out of 100 cars in a parking lot are white. What percent of the cars are white?

46 out of 100 children prefer strawberry ice cream. What percent of children do <u>NOT</u> prefer strawberry ice cream?

What does 100% represent?

What does more than 100% mean?

What does less than 100% mean?

EXAMPLES 9–12 Are the following common percents less than, equal to, or greater than one whole unit?

50%	225%
100%	150%

What is the procedure for finding the percent of a number using fractions?

To find $p\%$ of a number, …

Find 4% of 200.

EXAMPLE 13 A company produced 2500 personal computers, and 3% of them were defective. How many of the computers were defective?

Understand the problem

Create a plan

Find the answer

Check the answer

CONCEPT CHECK: Which percent below represents more than one whole unit?
99%, 2%, 101% or 50% ?

GUIDED EXAMPLES:

1. Write 62% as a fraction in simplest form.

2. Write $\dfrac{83}{100}$ as a percent.

3. Jackie has 100 marbles and 29 of them are red. What percent of the marbles are red?

4. A company produced 5000 digital cameras and 1% of them were defective. How many of the cameras were defective?

40

Notebook 6.5
Percent and Decimal Conversions

Recall: What does percent mean?

EXAMPLE 1 Write 51% as a decimal.

What is the procedure for writing a percent as a decimal?

Note: What do you do if there is no decimal point in the original percent?

CAUTION!! It may be necessary to insert zeros in order to …

EXAMPLES 2 – 5 Write each percent as a decimal.
135%

24.9%

$74\frac{1}{2}\%$

4.5%

EXAMPLE 6 Write 0.71 as a percent.

What is the procedure for writing a decimal as a percent?

CAUTION!! It may be necessary to add zeros in order to …

EXAMPLES 7–10 Write each decimal as a percent.
2.3

0.095

0.75

0.004

41

What is the procedure for finding the percent of a number?

For example, find 10% of 500.

EXAMPLE 11 A company made 7500 tables, and 20% of these tables were made from oak. How many of the tables were made from oak?

Understand the problem

Create a plan

Find the answer

Check the answer

CONCEPT CHECK: Carrie converted 0.53 to a percent and got an answer of 0.0053%. What was her mistake?

GUIDED EXAMPLES:

Write the percent as a decimal.

1. $9\frac{3}{4}\%$

2. $87\frac{1}{4}\%$

Write the decimal as a percent.

3. 0.225

4. A company made 6000 folders, and 5% of the folders were red. How many of the folders were red?

Notebook 6.6
Percent and Fraction Conversions

Recall: What does $p\%$ mean?

Recall: What are two ways you can convert $p\%$ to a fraction?
  1.

  2.

Note: Dividing p by _____ and multiplying p by _____ both result in the same answer.

EXAMPLE 1 Write 8% as a fraction in simplest form.

EXAMPLES 2–4 Write each percent as a fraction in simplest form.

Joe sells cars and receives $3\frac{1}{4}\%$ on each sale.

Property tax is $\frac{3}{10}\%$ off the estimated value.

The sales tax is 4.5% of the purchase price.

How do you write a fraction as a percent?
If the denominator is 100:

If the denominator is not 100:

EXAMPLES 5 & 6 Write each fraction as a percent.
  $\frac{32}{100}$

  $\frac{5}{8}$

EXAMPLE 7 Write as a percent. Round to the nearest tenth of a percent.
  $\frac{4}{7}$

43

Note: Rounding to the nearest tenth of a percent requires performing the division to _____ decimal places.

CAUTION!! When is rounding performed during a problem?

Summary:

Fraction	Decimal	Percent
$\dfrac{32}{100}$		
$\dfrac{5}{8}$		
$\dfrac{4}{7}$		

CONCEPT CHECK: If you are asked to solve a problem with the directions "write $\dfrac{6}{11}$ as a percent, rounded to the nearest tenth of a percent." What is the result before you round?

GUIDED EXAMPLES:
Write the % as a fraction in simplest form.
1. 65%

2. $\dfrac{1}{4}$%

Write the fraction as a percent. Round to the nearest tenth of a percent if necessary.

3. $\dfrac{3}{8}$

Name: _____ Date: _____

Instructor: _____ Section: _____

Notebook 6.7
The Percent Equation

What is the Percent Equation?

What does it look like in equation form?

"What amount   is   a percent   of   the whole?

Notes:

Usually "base" appears ….

"is" translates to …

"of" translates to …

Any of the quantities, _____, _____, or _____, can be the unknown quantity

Usually a is used for _____, p for the _____, and b for _____.

In symbols, the percent equation is _____.

EXAMPLES 1 & 2 Finding the amount.
What amount is 30% of 140?

60% of 90 is what amount?

EXAMPLES 3 & 4 Finding the base.
34 is 50% of what number?

60% of what number is 42?

EXAMPLE 5 45 is what percent of 180?

EXAMPLE 6 What percent of 30 is 10? Round to the nearest tenth of a percent.

Note: Rounding to the nearest tenth of a percent requires performing the division to _____ decimal places.

CAUTION!! True/False Rounding can be done at any time.

CONCEPT CHECK: For the problem "45 is 50 percent of what number," which quantity is unknown?

GUIDED EXAMPLES:
Use the percent equation to find the following. Round to the nearest tenth of a percent as needed.
1. What amount is 75% of 240?

2. 90 is 15% of what number?

3. 18 is what percent of 60?

4. 20 is what percent of 120?

Notebook 6.8
The Percent Proportion

What does the percent proportion state?

What is the percent proportion?
    Usually "base" appears ….

    Any of the quantities, _____, _____, or _____,
    can be the unknown quantity

    Usually a is used for _____, p for the _____,
    and b for _____.

    Since p is divided by 100, do we need to convert from a decimal?

Note: The percent proportion is an alternative to _____.

EXAMPLE 1 What amount is 20% of 85?
    Percent =

    Base =

    Find the amount:

EXAMPLE 2 21 is 10.5% of what number?
    Percent =

    Amount =

    Find the base:

EXAMPLE 3 83 is what percent of 332?
    Amount =

    Base =

    Find the percent:

EXAMPLE 4 4 is what percent of 48? Round to the nearest tenth of a percent.

Amount =

Base =

Find the percent:

CONCEPT CHECK: What is the unknown quantity in the problem "19 is 17% of what number"?

GUIDED EXAMPLES:

1. What amount is 25% of 64?

2. 25 is 12.5% of what number?

3. 12 is what percent of 60?

4. 30 is what percent of 45? Round to the nearest tenth of a percent.

Notebook 6.9
Percent Applications

Write the Percent Equation:

Write the Percent Proportion:

Note: Either the percent equation or the percent proportion can be used to solve problems involving _____.

Note: If you know the percent and the base, which one would be better to use?

Write the rule for finding the amount of sales tax and total cost.
Amount of Sales Tax =

Total Cost =

EXAMPLE 1 Eli purchased a wrist watch for $60. If the sales tax rate is 7%, how much sales tax did Eli pay? What was the total cost of the watch?
    Amount of sales tax:

    Total cost:

Write down the rule for finding the amount of discount and sale price.
Amount of Discount =

Sale Price =

EXAMPLE 2 Lucky's Shoes is having a 30% discount sale. How much will Jan save on a $40 pair of shoes? What is the sale price of the shoes?
    Amount of discount:

    Sale price:

Write the rule for finding the percent of change.

Percent of change =

EXAMPLE 3 Enrollment at the local high school went from 320 students to 480 students in one year? Find the percent of increase.

Amount of increase:

Percent change:

What do you know about simple interest?

It is often used in…

It uses an annual rate to calculate ….

It is usually calculated _____, not _____.

Write down the rule for finding simple interest and total amount paid.

Amount of interest =

Total amount paid =

Notes:

Principal is the amount of the _____.

The interest rate is the percent charged per year, expressed as a _____.

The amount of time must be expressed in _____.

EXAMPLE 4 Calculate the amount of interest and the total amount paid for a loan of $2000 for 3 years at a 4% annual rate of interest.

Interest:

Total amount paid:

CONCEPT CHECK: Arty is buying a $50 watch. Sales tax is 9.25%. What is his first step to calculate the total cost of the watch?

GUIDED EXAMPLES:

Alesha purchases a 3-speed bike for $450.

1. If the sales tax is 8%, how much sales tax did Alesha pay?

2. What was the total cost of his bike?

James bought a washer and dryer combination for $1100. He bought it on credit for 1 year at 6% simple interest.

3. Find the amount of interest James will pay.

4. Find the total cost of the washer and dryer, including interest.

Name: _____   Date: _____

Instructor: _____   Section: _____

Notebook 11.1
Introduction to Real Numbers

What are whole numbers?
What are integers?

_____ are numbers that can be written as a fraction of two integers. Give examples.

> Write a repeating decimal:
> Write a terminating decimal:

What are numbers that cannot be expressed as a fraction of two integers? Give examples.

True/False: All integers are rational numbers.

Rational numbers in decimal form are either _____
or _____.

The decimal form of an _____ is non-terminating and non-repeating. Give an example.

Define real numbers.

EXAMPLE 1 Classify each number as an integer, a rational number, an irrational number, and/or a real number.

Number	Integer	Rational Number	Irrational Number	Real Number
8				
$-\frac{1}{5}$				
1.65				
$\sqrt{3}$				
0.444…				
$\sqrt{9}$				

Any _____ can be plotted on a number line.

The real number line includes _____,
_____, and _____.

Label the three parts of the real number line:

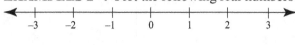

EXAMPLES 2–4 Plot the following real numbers on a number line.

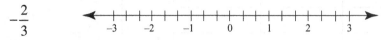

1

-2.75

½

Give some practical examples of real numbers.

EXAMPLES 5–7 Use a real number to represent each real life situation.
A temperature of 131.2° below zero is recorded in Antarctica.

The height of a mountain is 22,645 feet above sea level.

A golfer scored 5 under par in a recent tournament.

CONCEPT CHECK:
Give an example of a real-life negative number.

GUIDED EXAMPLES:
1. Classify the number as an integer, a rational number, an irrational number, and/or a real number. −6

2. Plot on a number line.

   $-\dfrac{2}{3}$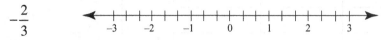

3. Plot on a number line.
   −0.75

4. Use a real number to represent the real life situation.
   An oil drilling platform extends 325 feet below sea level.

52

Name: _____   Date: _____

Instructor: _____   Section: _____

Notebook 11.2
Graphing Rational Numbers Using a Number Line

Every real number can be _____ on a number line.

EXAMPLES 1 & 2 Plot the following real numbers on a number line.

2

−1.5

An _____ is a statement that shows the relationship between any two real numbers that are not equal.

Which symbols are used to represent inequalities?

_____ is used to represent "is less than."

_____ is used to represent "is greater than."

EXAMPLES 3 & 4 Write the following statements using inequality symbols.

2 is less than 7

8 is greater than 5

Using a number line, one number is _____ another number if it is to the _____ of that number. Show this on a number line.

One number is _____ another number if it is to the _____ of that number on a number line. Show this on a number line.

True/False $3 > -1$ and $-1 < 3$ express the same meaning.

EXAMPLES 5–7 Plot the given numbers on a number line, and then replace the question mark with the appropriate symbol, < or >.

−2.5 ? 0

4 ? $\frac{3}{4}$

−1 ? −5

CONCEPT CHECK:
Correct or incorrect   0 > −1 can be read as "0 is less than −1"?

GUIDED EXAMPLES:
Plot each number on a number line.

1. −3.75

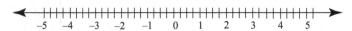

2. $\frac{3}{2}$

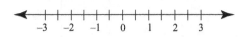

Write statements using inequality symbols.

3. −7 is less than 0

4. 3.5 is greater than 3

Name: _____   Date: _____

Instructor: _____   Section: _____

Notebook 11.3
Translating Phrases into Algebraic Inequalities

What is a variable?

To translate an everyday situation into an algebraic statement, each
_____ must be represented with a _____.

What is the symbol used for "is less than"?
What is the symbol used for "is greater than"?

What are the steps for translating words to symbols?
1. Determine …

2. Replace …

3. Replace …

EXAMPLE 1 Translate the phrase into an algebraic inequality.
A police officer claimed that a car was traveling at a speed more than 85 miles
per hour. (Use the variable s for speed.)

EXAMPLE 2 Translate the phrase into an algebraic inequality.
The bank loan officer said that the total consumer debt incurred by Hector and
Erica must be less than \$10,000 if they want to qualify for a mortgage to buy
their first home. (Use the variable d for debt.)

What is the difference between the symbols $<$ and $>$ and the symbols $\leq$ and $\geq$?

What phrase is represented by the symbol $\leq$?
What phrase is represented by $\geq$?

Key words to determine which symbols are most appropriate:

Less than or equal to

Greater than or equal to

EXAMPLE 3 Translate the phrases into an algebraic inequality.
The owner of a trucking company said that the payload of a truck must be no more than 4500 pounds. (Use the variable p for payload.)

EXAMPLE 4 Translate the phrases into an algebraic inequality.
Carlos must be at least 16 years old in order to get his driver's license. (Use the variable a for age.)

CONCEPT CHECK:
What symbol does the phrase "at most" or "no more than" translate to?

GUIDED EXAMPLES:
Translate the phrase into an algebraic inequality.
1. The height of a vehicle must be less than 7.5 feet in order to enter the parking garage. Use the variable h for the height.

2. According to the fire code, the room can hold at most 80 people. Use the variable n for the number of people.

3. A customer must be at least $4\frac{1}{2}$ feet tall in order to ride the roller coaster.

    Use the variable h for the customer's height.

4. During the heat wave, the high temperature was greater than 105° F. Use the variable T for the temperature.

Notebook 11.4
Finding the Absolute Value of a Real Number

Define absolute value.

EXAMPLES 1 & 2 Use a number line to find the absolute value of the following numbers.

3

−1.5

What is the symbol for absolute value?

How do you write the symbol form for absolute value of 5?

Write the absolute value of −2.87.

EXAMPLE 3 Write the expression for the absolute value of $-\dfrac{3}{8}$.

EXAMPLES 4–6 Find the absolute value of the following numbers.

$|-3.68|$

$|3.68|$

$|0|$

Note: Distance is always a _____, regardless of direction.
This means that the absolute value of any number will either be a
_____ _____ or _____.

EXAMPLES 7–9 Find the absolute value of the following numbers.

$|-8.333...|$

$\left|5\dfrac{9}{10}\right|$

$\left|-\dfrac{2}{7}\right|$

Note: The absolute value of a number can be thought of as the
_____ of the number, without regard to its
_____.

CONCEPT CHECK:
What is absolute value?

GUIDED EXAMPLES:

1. Find the absolute vale of –0.555.

2. Write the expression for the absolute value and then simplify. $\dfrac{4}{13}$

Simplify each absolute value.

3. $\left|-\dfrac{3}{10}\right|$

4. $|6.15|$

Name: _____   Date: _____

Instructor: _____   Section: _____

Notebook 12.1
Adding Real Numbers with the Same Sign

Banking Situation 1
You make a deposit of $20 on one day and a deposit of $15 the next day.
Represent on a number line the total value of your deposits.

Banking Situation 2
You write a check for $25 to pay your cell phone bill and two days later
you write a check for $5 to donate to a charity. Represent on a number line
the total value of the withdrawals.

Using the chip method, how do you represent a positive number?

Represent 3 using chips.
Represent –4 using chips.

EXAMPLES 1 & 2 Use chips to add the following.
$4 + 2$

$-2 + (-3)$

How do you add two numbers with the same sign?

EXAMPLE 3 Add. $8 + 4$
Add the numerical parts.

Give the answer the sign of the numbers being added.

Note: A number written without a sign is assumed to be _____.

EXAMPLE 4 Add. $-3 + (-5)$

EXAMPLE 5 Add. $-\dfrac{2}{3} + \left(-\dfrac{1}{7}\right)$

EXAMPLE 6 Add. $-8.1 + (-2.75) + (-5.03)$
Add from left to right.

CONCEPT CHECK:
When adding -0.25 and -0.66, what should be done first?

GUIDED EXAMPLES:

1. Add. $-3 + (-5)$

2. Add. $-5.18 + (-3.7)$

3. Add. $-\dfrac{3}{8} + \left(-\dfrac{3}{2}\right)$

4. Add. $-2 + (-7) + (-6)$

60

Name: _____   Date: _____

Instructor: _____   Section: _____

Notebook 12.2
Adding Real Numbers with Different Signs

Banking Situation 1
You make a deposit of $30 on one day, and on the next day you write a check for $25. Represent on a number line how the overall amount in your account changed after the deposit and withdrawal are processed.

Banking Situation 2
You make a deposit of $10 on one day, and on the next day you write a check for $40. Represent on a number line the overall change in the amount.

Using the chip method, a positive number is represented by _____
and a negative number is _____.

Represent 5 using chips.
Represent –3 using chips.
NOTICE: _____ + _____ = 0

EXAMPLES 1 & 2 Use chips to add the following.
6 + (–4)

–7 + 3

How do you add two numbers with different signs?

EXAMPLE 3 Add. –6 + 9
Subtract the numerical parts.

Give the answer the same sign
as the larger numerical part.

EXAMPLE 4 Add. $\dfrac{3}{8}+\left(-\dfrac{5}{7}\right)$

EXAMPLE 5 Add. $3.7 + (-10.5)$

EXAMPLE 6 Add. $-\dfrac{3}{4}+\dfrac{7}{9}$

CONCEPT CHECK:

Determine whether the final answer to the addition $(-8) + 7$ is negative or positive and indicate why.

GUIDED EXAMPLES:

Add the following.

1. $8 + (-5)$

2. $-11 + 7$

3. $2 + (-8)$

4. $-\dfrac{3}{11}+\dfrac{8}{11}$

62

Notebook 12.3
Finding the Opposite of a Real Number

Write the opposite of the following everyday situations:
A gain of 5 yards in a football game…

A check written for $28.50 on a checking account…

EXAMPLE 1 Find the opposite of the situation.
A temperature increase of 8.5°F
Opposite numbers are the _____ distance from zero but
in _____.

The opposite of 3 is _____.
The opposite of –3 is _____.

Represent the opposite numbers on the number line.
–2.16 and 2.16

–3 and 3

EXAMPLE 2 Find the opposite of the number using a number line. 8
Locate the number on a number line.

Find the number that is the same distance from zero, but in the opposite side.

Note: The _____ of a number is the _____ of that number.
The symbol for "the opposite of" a number is the _____ (or
_____) sign, "_____".

If a is a real number, then the opposite of a, denoted _____ equals

_____.

The opposite of _____ is _____.

What is the step for finding the opposite of a number?

EXAMPLES 3–5 Find the opposite of the number.
7

–3.5

$-\dfrac{5}{7}$

The _____ of a number is its distance from zero on a number line. The symbol is _____.

EXAMPLES 6 & 7 Find the opposite of the following absolute values.
$|5|$

$|-6.78|$

Why do pairs of opposite numbers have the same absolute value?

Any number plus is opposite is equal to _____.

What are additive inverses?

EXAMPLE 8 Find the additive inverse, or opposite, of the number. Then add the additive inverse to the number.
-4

CONCEPT CHECK:
What is the correct translation of the statement "The opposite of the absolute value of -1 is -1"?

GUIDED EXAMPLES:
1. Find the opposite of -6 using a number line.

Find the opposite of each of the following:

2. $-\dfrac{2}{3}$

3. $|-2|$

4. Find the additive inverse, or opposite, of each number. Then add the additive inverse to the number. $-\dfrac{5}{8}$

Notebook 12.4
Subtracting Real Numbers

Let's review addition
Write the rule for adding two numbers with the same sign.

Write the rule for adding two numbers with different signs.

Write the rule for subtracting real numbers.

We sometime refer to this as _____,_____,_____.

What are the steps for subtracting real numbers?
1.
2.
3.
4.

EXAMPLE 1 Subtract. $10 - 40$
Leave the first number alone.
Change the minus sign to a plus sign.
Change the sign of the number being subtracted.
Add the two numbers using the rules of addition.

EXAMPLE 2 Subtract. $8 - (-3)$

EXAMPLE 3 Subtract. $-5 - (-9)$.

EXAMPLE 4 Subtract. $-6.18 - 2.34$

OTHER NOTES

EXAMPLE 5 The temperature in a city is –8°F, and the temperature of a neighboring town is –15°F. Find the difference in temperature between the two cities.

CONCEPT CHECK:
Harry subtracted 7 – (–3) and got an answer of 4. This is incorrect. What was his error?

GUIDED EXAMPLES:
Subtract. Use "Add the Opposite."
1. 20 – 30

2. –2 – 9

Subtract. Use "Leave, Change, Change."
3. $\dfrac{13}{10} - \left(-\dfrac{7}{10} \right)$

4. –7 – (–2)

66

Name: _____   Date: _____

Instructor: _____   Section: _____

Notebook 12.5
Addition Properties of Real Numbers

What does the Commutative Property of Addition say?
_____ of the numbers being added does not change the sum.
Give examples:

What does the Addition Property of Zero say?
_____ to a number does not change the number.
Give examples:

What does the Associative Property of Addition say?
_____ when adding numbers does not change the sum.
Give examples:

Two numbers are _____, or _____, if they add to equal zero.

What does the Additive Inverse Property of Addition say?
The sum of a number and its additive inverse is equal to _____.
In symbols, for any real number a, $a + (-a) =$ ____ and $-a + a =$ ____.
Give examples:

EXAMPLES 1–5 Determine which property of addition is shown by each equation. The properties are the Commutative Property of Addition, the Associative Property of Addition, the Addition Property of Zero, and the Additive Inverse Property of Addition.

$0 + (-7) = -7$ _____

$(-2 + 3) + 5 = 5 + (-2 + 3)$ _____

$10 + (-10) = 0$ _____

$(-2 + 6) + 0.3 = -2 + (6 + 0.3)$ _____

$-\dfrac{2}{3} + \dfrac{1}{3} = \dfrac{1}{3} + \left(-\dfrac{2}{3}\right)$ _____

CONCEPT CHECK:
Which property is illustrated by $(-2) + 2 = 0$?

GUIDED EXAMPLES:
Determine which property of addition is shown by each equation. The properties are Commutative Property of Addition, the Associative Property of Addition, the Addition Property of Zero, and the Additive Inverse Property of Addition.

1. $-1 + (-9 + 5) = (-1 + (-9)) + 5$

2. $-5 + 6 = 6 + (-5)$

3. $7 + (-7) = 0$

4. $-\dfrac{1}{5} + \dfrac{1}{5} = 0$

Name: _____   Date: _____

Instructor: _____   Section: _____

Notebook 13.1
Multiplying Real Numbers

Complete the sign chart for multiplying signed numbers:

+	+	
+	−	
−	+	
−	−	

This chart applies for both _____ and _____.

Complete the chart for multiplying with different signs:

3	·	2	=	
3	·	1	=	
3	·	0	=	
3	·	−1	=	
3	·	−2	=	

Write the steps for multiplying two numbers with different signs.
To multiply two numbers with different signs,
1.

2.

EXAMPLE 1 Multiply. (7)(–4)
Multiply the numerical parts:
Determine the sign:

EXAMPLE 2 Multiply. $\left(-\dfrac{3}{4}\right)(5)$

Multiply the numerical parts:
Determine the sign:

Complete the chart for multiplying numbers with same sign:

−4	·	3	=	
−4	·	2	=	
−4	·	1	=	
−4	·	0	=	
−4	·	−1	=	

Write the steps for multiplying two numbers with the same sign.
To multiply two numbers with the same sign,
1.

2.

69

EXAMPLE 3 Multiply. (−12)(−9)
Multiply the numerical parts:
Determine the sign:

EXAMPLE 4 Multiply (−3.5)(−2)
Multiply the numerical parts:
Determine the sign:

EXAMPLES 5–8 Multiply.
(−3)(−4)

(−3)(−4)(−5)

(−3)(−4)(−5)(6)

(3)(−4)(−5)(6)

Notes: When multiplying an even number of negative factors, the product is
_____.

When multiplying an odd number of negative factors, the product is
_____.

CONCEPT CHECK:
What will be the sign of the product below?
$(+)(-)(-)(+)(+)(-)$

GUIDED EXAMPLES:
Multiply.
1. (14)(−8)

2. $\left(-2\dfrac{2}{3} \right)(8)$

3. (−3)(2)(5)(−4)

4. (−9)(4)(2)

Notebook 13.2
Finding the Reciprocal of a Real Number

What are reciprocals?

$\dfrac{b}{a}$ is the reciprocal of _____.

The reciprocal is also called the _____.

How do you find the reciprocal of a number?

Note: The reciprocal will have the _____ as
the _____.

Ex.   What is the reciprocal of $\dfrac{3}{4}$?

What is the reciprocal of $\dfrac{-13}{2}$?

A negative fraction can be written in _____ different
but _____ ways:

Note: How is a negative fraction typically written?

Examples of Negative Fractions

$\dfrac{-4}{2}$

$\dfrac{4}{-2}$

$-\dfrac{4}{2}$

EXAMPLE 1 Find the reciprocal. $-\dfrac{5}{7}$

Write the steps for finding the reciprocal of an integer.
1.

2.

What is the reciprocal of 0?
Why?

EXAMPLE 2 Find the reciprocal. -3

71

Write the steps for finding the reciprocal of a decimal.
To find the reciprocal of a decimal number,
1.

2.

3.

EXAMPLE 3 Find the reciprocal.   0.5

Write the steps for finding the reciprocal of a mixed number.
1.

2.

EXAMPLE 4 Find the reciprocal. $-4\dfrac{3}{5}$

CONCEPT CHECK:
True/False   To find the reciprocal of a fraction, invert (or flip) the fraction.

GUIDED EXAMPLES:
Find the reciprocal.

1. $\dfrac{9}{4}$

2. $-\dfrac{8}{11}$

3. -0.25

4. $-3\dfrac{3}{4}$

Notebook 13.3
Dividing Real Numbers

What is division?

What is the answer to a division problem?

The number being divided is the _____.
The number you are dividing by is the _____.

What are the two ways we can write division? Use the terms divisor, dividend, and quotient.

Write the procedure for dividing signed numbers?

How do you determine the sign of the answer (quotient)?

EXAMPLES 1–3 Divide.

$-21 \div (-7)$

$3.2 \div 0.8$

$\dfrac{-45}{25}$

EXAMPLE 4 Four friends decide to start a business together. They share a startup loan of $120,000. If they split the amount of the loan equally between them, how much does each friend owe?

Recall dividing fractions.
What is the rule for dividing by a fraction?

How do you divide by a mixed number?

EXAMPLES 5 & 6 Divide.

$$32 \div \left(-\frac{8}{3}\right)$$

$$-\frac{11}{6} \div 2\frac{4}{9}$$

CONCEPT CHECK:

Which of the following expressions has a negative quotient?

a. $\frac{0}{-12}$ b. $\frac{-48}{-6}$ c. $\frac{16}{-8}$ d. $\frac{35}{7}$

GUIDED EXAMPLES:

Divide.

1. $-90 \div (-18)$

2. $42 \div (-0.7)$

3. $\left(-\frac{4}{5}\right) \div \left(-\frac{7}{3}\right)$

4. $\left(-9\frac{1}{3}\right) \div \left(-3\frac{1}{2}\right)$

Notebook 13.4
Exponents and the Order of Operations

Why do we use exponents?
What is the base?
What is the exponent?

Write the exponential form of $2\cdot2\cdot2\cdot2$.

EXAMPLE 1 Write in exponential form.

$$\left(-\frac{5}{7}\right)\left(-\frac{5}{7}\right)\left(-\frac{5}{7}\right)\left(-\frac{5}{7}\right)$$

Caution! When the base is _____, be careful in determining the sign
of the _____-.

EXAMPLES 2 & 3 Evaluate.
$(-4)^2$

$(-4)^3$

Sign Rule for Exponents
     A _____ base raised to an even power is _____.
     A _____ base raised to an odd power is _____.

Caution! Be careful with exponents and negative signs.
     What does $(-2)^4$ mean?

     What does -2^4 mean?

     Do you see the difference???

EXAMPLE 4 Evaluate.

$$\left(-\frac{2}{5}\right)^3$$

Any non-zero number raised to the zero power is equal to _____.
Any number raised to the power of 1 is equal to _____.

EXAMPLES 5 & 6 Evaluate.
$(-94)^0$

$(-23)^1$

EXAMPLES 7 & 8 Evaluate.

$(-5)^2$

$-\left(-\dfrac{1}{5}\right)^3$

Write the steps for Order of Operations.

1. P:
2. E:
3. MD:
4. AS:

EXAMPLES 9 & 10 Evaluate.

$\dfrac{4^3 + 2(-5)}{2^3}$

$(-4)^2 - 2(5)^2$

EXAMPLE 11 Evaluate.

$2^6 \div 2^3 - [(3)^2 + 5 - (27)^0]^2$

CONCEPT CHECK:

For the expression -5^4, identify the base.

GUIDED EXAMPLES:

Evaluate.

1. $-\left(\dfrac{18}{73}\right)^1$

2. $(-0.6)^4$

3. $\dfrac{-3^3 + 2^2(7)}{-(-6)^2}$

76

Name: _____   Date: _____

Instructor: _____   Section: _____

Notebook 13.5
The Distributive Property

See egg carton example. Write down any notes you need.

What does the Distributive Property say?

Examples
$-7(3 + 5)$

$2(5 - 7)$

EXAMPLE 1 Multiply. $9 \cdot 103$

  Rewrite as an addition problem.
  Use Distributive Property to multiply.
  Simplify.

When is the distributive property most useful?

The Distributive Property can be used to _____.

EXAMPLE 2 Multiply. $2(x + 3)$

  Rewrite using Distributive Property.
  Answer.

EXAMPLE 3 Multiply.
$-3(-8x + 3)$

EXAMPLES 4–7 Multiply.
$2(-4y + 7)$

$-9(-4x - 6)$

$-(x - 2)$

$5(3x + 2y - 6z)$

CONCEPT CHECK:

Write a situation that is appropriate to use the Distributive Property.

GUIDED EXAMPLES:

1. Simplify using the Distributive Property. $5(3 + 8)$

2. Multiply using the Distributive Property. $8 \cdot 17$

3. Multiply. $-2(x - 3)$

4. Simplify using the Distributive Property. $4(x + 3y - 7z)$

Notebook 13.6
Multiplication Properties of Real Numbers

State the Commutative Property of Multiplication.
_____ when multiplying numbers
does not change the result. In symbols, _____.
Give examples:

State the Associative Property of Multiplication.
_____ when multiplying numbers does not
change the product. In symbols, _____.
Give examples:

State the Identity Property of Multiplication.
Multiplying a number by one results in _____.
In symbols, $1 \cdot a =$ ____ and $a \cdot 1 =$ _____.
Give examples:

EXAMPLES 1–4 Determine which property of multiplication is shown by
each equation. The properties are the Commutative Property of Multiplication,
the Associative Property of Multiplication, or the Identity Property of
Multiplication.

$(-17)(1) = -17$ _____

$(-4 \cdot 2) \cdot 3 = -4 \cdot (2 \cdot 3)$ _____

$(6.5)(-2) = (-2)(6.5)$ _____

$(2)(3 \cdot 6) = (2 \cdot 3)(6)$ _____

Why would you want to change the order of factors or change the grouping of
the numbers?

EXAMPLE 5 Multiply.
$\left(\dfrac{1}{4}\right)(-5)(-4)(3)$

CONCEPT CHECK:

Which property of multiplication represents changing the order?

GUIDED EXAMPLES:

Find each product and determine which property of multiplication is used.

1. $12 \cdot 41 = 41 \cdot 12$

2. $(-4 \cdot 5) \cdot 7 = -4 \cdot (5 \cdot 7)$

3. Rewrite using the indicated property, and simplify. $(-3x)(-5)$

4. Multiply. $\left(-\dfrac{1}{2}\right)\left(\dfrac{4}{9}\right)(2)(-9)$

80

Notebook 14.1
Introduction to Expressions

How long would three 4-foot-long pieces of rope be if they were laid end-to-end?

How long would three 8-foot-long pieces of rope be, laid end-to-end?

What about three 11-foot-long pieces of rope?

What is a variable?

If the length of each piece of rope is unknown, how would you express the length of three pieces of this rope laid end-to-end?

What if one piece of rope was 2-feet-long and another piece of unknown length?

What are two examples of algebraic expressions used to represent the total length of rope pieces?

An _____ is a combination of _____ and _____, _____ and grouping symbols.

List some examples of algebraic expressions:

A _____ is any number, _____, or _____ of numbers
and/or variables. How are terms separated?

True/False The sign in front of the term is considered part of the term.

EXAMPLES 1–5 Identify the terms in each expression.
$3x$

$2x + 1$

$-7xy^2 + 3z - 2$

60

$-6x - 4z$

What are like terms?

Like terms have exactly the same _____ _____.

EXAMPLES 6–10 Identify the like terms in each expression.

$3x + 4y - 7x + 5z$

$2x^2 + 3x$

$-4x + 5 - 2x - 7$

$2x^2 + 3x - 1 + 6x^2 - 9x + 8$

$8a - 7b + 3b + 2b + a$

CONCEPT CHECK:

For the algebraic expression $-5y^2 + 6x - 3xy + 2$, is $6x$ a term in the expression?

GUIDED EXAMPLES:

Identify the terms in each expression.

1. $6y$

2. $-5ab^2 + 2c - 6$

Identify the like terms in each expression.

3. $3a + 5b - 9a + 3c$

4. $7x + 3y - 2x + 9y - 4$

Notebook 14.2
Evaluating Algebraic Expressions

How do you find the perimeter of a square?

What expression is used to represent this?

Find the perimeter of a square with a side of 27 feet.

What does the value of an expression depend on?

Write the steps for evaluating an algebraic expression.
1.

2.

EXAMPLE 1 Evaluate $3x + 6$ for $x = 4$.
Substitute the given value.
Simplify.

EXAMPLE 2 Evaluate $5x^2$ for $x = 6$.
Substitute the given value.
Simplify.

EXAMPLE 3 Evaluate $3y^2 - y$ for $y = -7$.
Substitute the given value.
Simplify.

EXAMPLE 4 Evaluate $\dfrac{a + 2b}{4c}$ for $a = 0$, $b = -6$, and $c = 2$.
Substitute the given values.
Simplify.

Note: Use the Distributive Property to rewrite $2(l + w)$.

EXAMPLE 5 The perimeter of a rectangle can be found by the expression $2(\underline{l} + w)$ or $2l + 2w$, where l is the length and w is the width. Find the perimeter of this rectangle if $l = 5.4$ and $w = 8$. You will need to label the rectangle.)

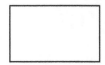

CONCEPT CHECK:
When evaluating an algebraic expression, the value of the expression depends on the value of the _____.

GUIDED EXAMPLES:
Evaluate for the given values.
1. $7m + 2$ for $m = 1$

2. $\dfrac{3a - 4b}{2c}$ for $a = 9$, $b = 7$, and $c = -3$

3. $9d^2$ for $d = 4$

4. $6w^2 + 3w$ for $w = -5$

Notebook 14.3
Simplifying Expressions

An _____ is a combination of _____ and _____, operation symbols and _____.

What would you get if you combined 5 inches and 6 inches?

Could you combine 4 inches and 3 square feet?   Why?

How do you simplify an expression?

EXAMPLES 1–4 Combine like terms.

$13x - 2x$

$-4a + 3b + 9a$

$2x^3 + 9x^2 - x + 7$

$\dfrac{4}{3}m + \dfrac{2}{3}m - m$

Why might it be helpful to rearrange the terms when simplifying expressions?

Caution! The sign _____ of the term stays with the term.

EXAMPLE 5 Combine like terms. $2a + 32b - 25c - 12b + 15a + 13c$
Rearrange the terms.

Combine the like terms.

EXAMPLE 6 Combine like terms. $15x^3 + 2 - 8x^2 + x^3 - 9x + 13x^2 - 3$
Rearrange the terms.

Combine the like terms.

EXAMPLE 7 Combine like terms. $16x^2y - 3xy^2 + 5xy - 2x^2y - 4xy^2$
Rearrange the terms.

Combine the like terms.

CONCEPT CHECK:
What does it mean to combine like terms?

GUIDED EXAMPLES:
Combine like terms.
1. $23x + 6x$

2. $6x^2 + 18y - 4x^2 + 12y$

3. $6a^2 + 14a - 19a^2 - 34b - 8b + 4a + 15b + a$

4. $12ab^2 + 6.5ab - 5a^2b - 4ab^2 + ab$

86

Notebook 14.4
Simplifying Expressions with Parentheses

What are some types of grouping symbols used in expressions?

What does it mean if an algebraic expression is simplified?

If an algebraic expression contains parentheses, what can be done to remove parentheses?

EXAMPLE 1 Simplify.
$5 + 4(a + b)$

What does a negative sign in front of the parentheses mean?

How do you simplify an expression with a negative sign in front of the parentheses?

EXAMPLES 2 & 3 Simplify.
$-(4x - 3y)$

$-(5 + 6a)$

Write the steps for simplifying algebraic expressions.
1.

2.

3.

EXAMPLES 4 & 5 Simplify.
$8x - 3(4x - 5)$

$2[3(9x - 8)]$

EXAMPLE 6 Simplify.

$14x - 2[3x + 3(5)]$

_____ are also considered grouping symbols.

EXAMPLE 7 Simplify. $\dfrac{7-(4-x)}{3+2(x-5)}$

Simplify the numerator.

Simplify the denominator.

CONCEPT CHECK:

How are parentheses removed?

GUIDED EXAMPLES:

Simplify.

1. $7 + 2(m + n)$

2. $-(7a + 6b)$

3. $7x + 3[2x + 2(6x - 1)]$

4. $\dfrac{4(3x-14)}{9(5y+2)}$

Notebook 14.5
Translating Words into Symbols

What does the Commutative Property of Addition state?

What does the Commutative Property of Multiplication state?

True/False The order in which you add or multiply two numbers does not matter.

List some key words (phrases) for addition representing "$x + 4$"
The _____ of a number and four   A number _____ by four
Four _____ a number   Four is _____ a number
Four _____ a number   A number _____ four.

List some key words (phrases) for multiplication representing "$2x$":
_____ a number   _____ a number
The _____ of two and a number   Two _____ a number
Two _____ a number

EXAMPLES 1–3 Translate into an algebraic expression.
The sum of 8 and a number

Triple a number

75% of a number

List some key words (phrases) for subtraction representing "$a - 6$"
The _____ a number and six   Six is _____ a number
A number _____ by six   Six _____ a number
Six _____ a number   A number _____ six

List some key words (phrases) for division representing "$\dfrac{a}{7}$":

A number _____ seven
The _____ of a number and seven
A number _____ seven

Caution! Which operations do not work with the Commutative Property? What does this mean?

EXAMPLES 4–7 Translate into an algebraic expression.
Five less than twelve

Twelve less than five

Fifty divided by one

One divided by fifty

EXAMPLES 8–10 Translate into an algebraic expression. Use n for the variable.
Twelve less than a number n

The difference between -9 and a number n

The quotient of a number n and 2.1

EXAMPLES 11–13 Translate into an algebraic expression. Use parentheses if necessary.
Seven more than double a number x

A number x is tripled and then increased by 8

One-half of the sum of a number and 3

EXAMPLE 14 Use an expression to describe the measure of each angle. The figure is not drawn to scale. The measure of the second angle of a triangle is double the measure of the first angle, and the third angle is 15° more than the measure of the second angle. You will need to draw the triangle.

CONCEPT CHECK:
What phrase best represents $2(n - 3)$?

GUIDED EXAMPLES:
Translate into an algebraic expression.
1. A number increased by thirty-eight

2. Fifteen less than a number

3. The quotient of a number and 5.5

4. A number x out of sixty-two

Notebook 15.1
Translating Words into Equations

A _____ is a letter or symbol that is used to represent an unknown quantity.

What are the basic steps for understanding word problems.

a.

b.

c.

What is an equation?
What is it that all equations contain?

What are the steps for writing an equation from a word problem?

a.

b.

c.

d.

e.

EXAMPLE 1 Translate the following into an equation. Let n represent the number.
One-third of a number is fourteen.

EXAMPLE 2 Translate the following into an equation. Do not solve.
Five more than six times a number is three hundred five.

EXAMPLE 3 Translate the following into an equation. Do not solve.
The larger of two numbers is three more than twice the smaller number.
The sum of the numbers is thirty-nine.

Understand the problem.

Write the equation.

EXAMPLE 4 Translate the following into an equation. Do not solve.
The annual snowfall in Juneau, Alaska, is 105.8 inches. This is 20.2 inches less than three times the annual snowfall in Boston, Massachusetts.

Understand the problem.

Write the equation.

CONCEPT CHECK:

Is $\dfrac{28x}{9}$ an equation?

GUIDED EXAMPLES:
Translate into an equation. Do not solve.
1. One-fourth of a number is eleven.

2. Six more than three times a number is fifty-seven.

3. Four times a number decreased by thirteen is thirty-five.

4. The larger of two numbers is eleven more than three times the smaller number. The sum of the numbers is forty-two.

Notebook 15.2
Linear Equations and Solutions

An _____ is a mathematical statement that two _____ are _____.

What are some examples of equations?

What is a letter or symbol that represents an unknown quantity?

Example "Five more than a number is equal to eight."

What is a solution of an equation?

What is a solution of $x + 5 = 8$?   How do you know?

How many solutions does an equation have?

Write the steps for determining if a given value is a solution.
1.

2.

3.

EXAMPLE 1 Is 2 a solution of the equation $3x - 1 = 5$?
Substitute.

Simplify.

True?

EXAMPLES 2 & 3
Is -1 a solution of the equation $2x + 6 = -1$?

Is -3 a solution to $7x - 2 = 5$?

Define a linear equation in one variable.

EXAMPLES 4–6 Determine if each equation is a linear equation.

$2x + 3 = 1$

$2x = 5$

$6x^2 - 3 = 4$

CONCEPT CHECK:
Why is 0 not a solution to the equation $2x + 1 = 5$?

GUIDED EXAMPLES:
1. Is 9 a solution of the equation $4x - 11 = 25$?

2. Is –5 a solution of the equation $4 = 7x - 2$?

3. Is –4 a solution of the equation $5x + 3 = -17$?

4. Determine if $2x - 9 = -15$ is a linear equation.

Notebook 15.3
Using the Addition Property of Equality

A _____ of an equation is the number(s) that, when substituted for the
_____, makes the equation _____.

To determine if a given value is a _____ of an equation,
_____ this value into the equation and _____ each side
according to the order of operations.

What are equivalent equations?

When an equation is in the form $x =$ some number, that number is the
_____ of the equation.

What is the process of finding the solution(s) of an equation called?

What is the goal of solving an equation?

The Addition Property of Equality states that if the _____
number is added to _____ of an equation, the results
on both sides are _____ in value. That is, adding the _____
_____ to both sides of an equation does not change the _____.

How is this represented in symbols?

Does this property work for subtraction as well?   Why or why not?

Which property "undoes" addition?
Which property "undoes" subtraction?

EXAMPLE 1 Solve for x. Check your solution.
$x + 16 = 20$

Write the steps for solving an equation using the addition property.

1.

2.

3.

EXAMPLE 2 Solve for x. Check your solution.
$-14 = x - 3$

EXAMPLE 3 Solve for x. Check your solution.
$x - \dfrac{1}{2} = -\dfrac{5}{2}$

When solving an equation, _____ both sides of the equation whenever possible. _____ will make it easier to work with.

EXAMPLE 4 Solve for x. Check your solution.
$15 + 2 = 3 + x + 6$

CONCEPT CHECK:
What would the first calculation be in order to solve the equation
$2 - 8 = 2x + 9$?

GUIDED EXAMPLES:
Solve for x. Check your solution.

1. $\dfrac{8}{5} = x - \dfrac{2}{5}$

2. $x + 0.6 = -8.1$

3. $5 + x - 3 = -2 + 7$

4. $27 + x - 14 = -5 + 39$

96

Name: _____   Date: _____

Instructor: _____   Section: _____

Notebook 15.4
Using the Multiplication Property of Equality

How does the Addition Property of Equality help to solve an equation?

The Multiplication Property of Equality states that if both sides of an
_____ are _____ by the _____ number, the
_____ does not change.

How is this represented in symbols?

Does this property work for division as well?   Why or why not?

Caution! We cannot divide by _____. So we must restrict our divisors to
_____ numbers.

_____ and _____ are reverse operations.

EXAMPLE 1 Solve for x. Check your solution.
$$\frac{x}{3} = -15$$

Write the steps for solving an equation using the multiplication property.
1.

2.

3.

EXAMPLE 2 Solve for x. Check your solution.
$3x = 21$

97

EXAMPLE 3 Solve for x. Check your solution.

$20 = -4x$

When solving an equation, _____ both sides of the equation whenever possible. _____ will make it easier to work with.

EXAMPLE 4 Solve for x. Check your solution.

$2x - 5x = -12$

CONCEPT CHECK:

What is the reverse operation of multiplication?

GUIDED EXAMPLES:

Solve for x. Check your solution.

1. $-18 = 6x$

2. $-5x = 35$

3. $\dfrac{x}{10} = -6$

4. $8x - 9x = 10$

Notebook 15.5
Using the Addition and Multiplication Properties Together

Jenny scored several goals in field hockey during April. Her teammates scored three more than five times the number of goals she scored. Her teammates scored 18 goals. How many goals did Jenny score?

What equation do we need to solve?

The properties of equality state that you can _____ (or _____)
and _____ (or _____) both sides of an equation
by the_____ without changing the _____.

EXAMPLE 1 Solve for x to determine how many goals Jenny scored, and then check your solution. Be sure to show all steps.
$5x + 3 = 18$

Write the steps for solving an equation of the form $ax + b = c$.
1. Get the _____ alone on one side of the equation.

2. Get the _____ alone on one side of the equation.

3. Simplify any _____, if needed.

4. _____ your solution.

EXAMPLE 2 Solve for x. Show all steps.
$$-\frac{1}{2}x + 10 = 16$$

EXAMPLE 3 Solve for x. Then check. Show all steps.

$6x - 8 = -2$

EXAMPLE 4 Solve for x. Then check. Show all steps.

$4 = -7 + 8x$

CONCEPT CHECK:

Erica and Stefan played a video game. Erica scored 8 less than 4 times Stefan's score. Erica's score was 1000 points. Let x = the number of points Stefan scored. Write the equation that finds the number of points Stefan scored.

GUIDED EXAMPLES:

Solve for x. Check your solution.

1. $9x + 1 = 28$

2. $\dfrac{1}{8}x - 6 = -10$

3. $-15 = 2x - 7$

4. $3x - 5.6 = 12.4$

Notebook 16.1
Solving Equations with Variables on Both Sides

A _____ of an equation is the number(s) that, when substituted for the _____, makes the equation true.

The process of finding the solution(s) to an equation is called _____.

What is the goal of solving an equation?

The properties of equality state that you can _____ (or _____) and _____ (or _____) both sides of an equation by the _____ without changing the _____.

How do you know whether to add or subtract to get the variable terms on one side of the equation?

EXAMPLE 1 Solve for x. Check your answer.
$9x = 6x + 15$
Get the variable terms on one side.

Get the number terms on the other side.

Get the variable alone on one side.

Simplify.

EXAMPLE 2 Solve for x. Check your answer. Show all steps.
$9x + 4 = 7x - 2$
Get the variable terms on one side.

Get the number terms on the other side.

Get the variable alone on one side.

Simplify.

You can simplify one or both sides of the equation by _____ like terms that are on the _____ of the equation.

EXAMPLE 3 Solve for x. Check your answer. Show all steps.

$5x + 26 - 6 = 9x + 12x$

Simplify each side.

Get the variable terms on one side.

Get the number terms on the other side.

Get the variable alone on one side.

Simplify.

EXAMPLE 4 Solve for x. Check your answer. Show all steps.

$-x + 8 - x = 3x + 10 - 3$

Simplify each side.

Get the variable terms on one side.

Get the number terms on the other side.

Get the variable alone on one side.

Simplify.

CONCEPT CHECK:

What is the first goal when solving an equation with a variable m on both sides?

GUIDED EXAMPLES:

Solve for x.

1. $5x + 8 = 10x$

2. $7x - 7 = 12x + 8$

3. $11x + 6x = -20 + 13x - 12$

4. $-13x + 3 + 5x = 1 - 6x + 16$

102

Name: _____   Date: _____

Instructor: _____   Section: _____

Notebook 16.2
Solving Equations with Parentheses

Recall: For all real numbers a, b, and c,
$a(b + c) =$ _____.(Distributive Property)

In order to solve an equation with parentheses, _____
first using the _____to remove parentheses.

EXAMPLE 1 Solve for x. Check your answer. Show all steps.
$2(x + 5) = -12$
Simplify each side.
Get the variable terms on one side.
Get the number terms on the other side
Get the variable alone on one side.
Simplify.

EXAMPLE 2 Solve for x. Check your answer. Show all steps.
$-5(x - 3) + 7 = x - 8$
Simplify each side.
Get the variable terms on one side.
Get the number terms on the other side
Get the variable alone on one side.
Simplify.

EXAMPLE 3 Solve for x. Check your answer. Show all steps.
$5(x + 1) - 3(x - 3) = 17$
Simplify each side.
Get the variable terms on one side.
Get the number terms on the other side.
Get the variable alone on one side.
Simplify.

EXAMPLE 4 Solve for x. Check your answer. Show all steps.
$3(-x - 7) = -2(2x + 5)$
Simplify each side.
Get the variable terms on one side.
Get the number terms on the other side.
Get the variable alone on one side.
Simplify.

EXAMPLE 5 Solve for x. Check your answer. Show all steps.

$3(0.5x - 4.2) = 0.6(x - 12)$

Simplify each side.

Get the variable terms on one side

Get the number terms on the other side.

Get the variable alone on one side.

Simplify.

EXAMPLE 6 Solve for x. Check your answer. Show all steps.

$2(18x - 5) + 2 = 24x - 3(12x + 8)$

Simplify each side.

Get the variable terms on one side.

Get the number terms on the other side.

Get the variable alone on one side.

Simplify.

CONCEPT CHECK:

What is the correct application of the Distributive Property for

$5(x - 3) - 2(x + 1) = 15$?

GUIDED EXAMPLES:

Solve for x.

1. $3(x - 7) = 6$

2. $5(-2x + 1) = -7(x - 2)$

3. $4(-2x - 3) = -5(x - 2) + 2$

4. $5(10x - 1) + 7 = 35x - 4(5x + 3)$

104

Notebook 16.3
Solving Equations with Fractions

The _____ (LCD) of two or more fractions is
the _____ (LCM) of the _____ of the
fractions.

True/False The equation-solving procedures are the same for equations with or
without fractions.

When solving equations with fractions, we can perform an extra step that will
make the calculations a little "nicer". What is this extra step?

EXAMPLE 1 Solve for x. Check your answer. Show all steps.

$$\frac{1}{4}x - \frac{2}{3} = \frac{5}{12}x$$

Find the LCD of the fractions.
Multiply both sides by the LCD.
Use the Distributive Property.
Solve.

Note: Multiplying both sides of the equation by the LCD and using
_____ is the same as _____ each term
in the equation by the _____.

EXAMPLE 2 Solve for x. Check your answer. Show all steps.

$$\frac{x}{3} + 3 = \frac{x}{5} - \frac{1}{3}$$

Find the LCD of the fractions.
Multiply each term by the LCD.
Solve.

EXAMPLE 3 Solve for x. Check your answer. Show all steps.

$$\frac{x+5}{7} = \frac{x}{4} + \frac{1}{2}$$

Find the LCD of the fractions.

Multiply each term by the LCD.

Solve.

How can you use this to solve equations containing decimals?

EXAMPLE 4 Solve for x. Check your answer. Show all steps.

$0.6x - 1.3 = 4.1$

Multiply each term by 10.

Solve.

Why did we choose to multiply by 10?
How do you know what to multiply by?

CONCEPT CHECK: To make the process of solving $\dfrac{1}{2}x - 4x = \dfrac{1}{3}x$ easier,

by what number can both sides of equation be multiplied?

GUIDED EXAMPLES:
Solve for x.

1. $\dfrac{2}{3}x + \dfrac{1}{2} = -\dfrac{5}{6}$

2. $2 - \dfrac{x}{10} = -\dfrac{x}{4} + \dfrac{1}{2}$

3. $\dfrac{x+6}{9} = \dfrac{x}{6} + \dfrac{1}{2}$

4. $-2.7x + 6.4 = -4(3x - 1.6)$

106

Notebook 16.4
Solving a Variety of Equations

Write the steps for solving an equation:

1. Remove _____ by using _____.

2. If _____ or _____ remain, multiply each
   term by the _____ of all fractions.

3. _____ each side if possible.

4. _____ or _____ terms on both sides to get all
   _____ on one side of the equation.

5. _____ or _____ number terms on both sides to get all
   _____ on the OTHER side of the equation.

6. _____ or _____ both sides of the equation to get the
   _____ alone on one side of the equation.

7. _____ the solution.

8. _____ your solution.

True/False Every step of the procedure is needed in each problem.

EXAMPLE 1 Solve for *x*. Check your answer. Show all steps.
$3(6x - 4) = 4(3x + 9)$

EXAMPLE 2 Solve for *x*. Check your answer. Show all steps.
$2(3x + 1) = 5(x - 2) + 3$

EXAMPLE 3 Solve for *x*. Check your answer. Show all steps.

$$\frac{1}{3}(x - 2) = \frac{1}{5}(x + 4) + 2$$

What does it mean if an equation has no solution?
What symbol is used for no solution?

What is a contradiction?

EXAMPLE 4 Solve for x. Check your answer. Show all steps.
$5(x + 3) = 2x - 8 + 3x$

What is an identity?

What does it mean if an equation has an infinite number of solutions?

EXAMPLE 5 Solve for x. Check your answer. Show all steps.
$9x - 8x - 7 = 3 + x - 10$

CONCEPT CHECK:
When the equation $2x - x + 1 = x + 3 - 2$ is solved, the result is $1 = 1$.
True/False The equation is an identity.

GUIDED EXAMPLES:
Solve for x.

1. $\frac{1}{5}(5x - 10) = \frac{1}{3}(9x + 6)$

2. $\frac{1}{2}(x + 5) = \frac{1}{5}(x - 2) + \frac{1}{2}$

3. $-1 + 5(x - 2) = 12x + 3 - 7x$

4. $9(x + 3) - 6 = 24 - 2x - 3 + 11x$

Notebook 16.5
Solving Equations and Formulas for a Variable

What is a formula?

Write some examples for formulas.

What is the procedure for solving a formula for a specified formula?

1. Identify the _____.

2. Remove any _____.

3. If fractions or decimals remain, _____ each term by the _____ of all fractions.

4. _____ each side if possible.

5. _____ terms on both sides to get all terms containing the specified variable on _____ of the equation.

6. _____ terms on both sides of the equation to get all terms NOT containing the _____ on the other side.

7. _____ both sides of the equation to get the specified _____ alone on one side of the equation.

What is the hint for solving a formula for a specified variable, treat…

EXAMPLE 1 Solve $5x + 2 = 17$ and $ax + b = c$ for x.

EXAMPLE 2 Solve for t. $d = rt$

EXAMPLES 3–6 Solve for the specified variable.

$C = 2\pi r$, solve for r

$a = \dfrac{v}{t}$, solve for v

$x + y = 8$, solve for x

$a - b = -3$, solve for a

EXAMPLES 7 & 8 Solve for the specified variable.

$5x + 3y = 6$, solve for y

$y = mx + b$, solve for x

CONCEPT CHECK:

True/False $P = 2L + 2W$ can be solved for W using only the Multiplication Property of Equality.

GUIDED EXAMPLES:

1. Solve for r. $I = prt$

2. Solve for l. $P = 2l + 2w$

3. Solve for x. $x + 3y = 7$

4. Solve for y. $5x - 2y = -8$

Notebook 16.6
Solving and Graphing Linear Inequalities

Review of Inequalities
A _____ is a statement that shows the relationship between any two real numbers that are _____ _____.

Fill in the table:

Symbol	Phrase
<	
>	
≤	
≥	

What is a linear inequality?
Examples of linear inequalities:

What is a solution of an inequality?

What does the inequality $x > 3$ mean?

What is the graph of an inequality?

Write the steps for graphing a linear inequality.
1. Plot the _____.
     a.
     b.
2. Shade _____ …

EXAMPLES 1 & 2 Graph each inequality on a number line.

$x > 3$

$x \leq -1$

When do you use an open circle on the graph and when do you use a closed circle on a graph?

What does it mean to solve an inequality?

What happens to an inequality when you add 2, subtract 2, multiply by 2 and divide by 2 on both sides of an inequality?

What happens when you add -2 or subtract -2 to both sides?

What happens when you multiply or divide both sides of an inequality by a negative number?

To solve a linear inequality, use the same procedure used to solve an equation, except, the _____ of an inequality must be _____ if you _____ or _____ both sides by a _____.

EXAMPLE 3 Solve and graph the inequality. $5x + 2 < 12$

EXAMPLE 4 Solve and graph the inequality. $5 - 4x \geq -7$

CONCEPT CHECK:

What is the word phrase that translates to $x \geq 3$?

GUIDED EXAMPLES:

Graph the inequality on a number line.

1. $x > 5$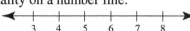

2. $-2x - 6 < 0$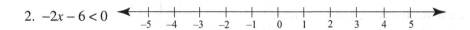

Solve and graph the inequality.

3. $7 + 4x \leq 5$

4. $2(x - 9) \geq -4(x - 6)$

112

E Introduction to Problem Solving
Vocabulary

Algebraic expressions with addition as the operation

The sum of x and 2	7 plus a	5 added to y	3 greater than m
$x+2$	$7+a$	$y+5$	$m+3$

Algebraic expressions with subtraction as the operation

The difference of 20 and r	50 minus p	15 less than w
$20-r$	$50-p$	$w-15$

a decreased by b	8 reduced by m	x subtracted from 90
$a-b$	$8-m$	$90-x$

Algebraic expressions with multiplication as the operation

The product of 13 and a	3 times b	twice x	Half of x
$13a$	$3b$	$2x$	$(1/2)x$

Algebraic expressions with division as the operation

The quotient of 7 and a	A divided by B	The ratio of x to 11
$7/a$	A/B	$x/11$

EXAMPLES

Write an equation for each word problem and then solve.

1. Find two consecutive odd numbers whose sum is 36.

If the first number is: x

The second consecutive odd number would be: _____

The equation is: _____ + _____ $= 36$

Solve for x:

Write an equation for each word problem and then solve.

2. Six more than three times a certain number is equal to twelve
   less than nine times the number. What is the number?

The equation is:

The number is:

3. Tom sold a camera on Craigslist for $85.00. This was $30 more than half the amount he paid for it. What price did he pay for the camera?

The equation is:

The price of the camera:

4. Ashley paid a $900.50 bill for four new tires. This included $217 for each of the new tires and $26 an hour for installation. Find the number of hours it took to install the new tires.

The equation is:

The number of hours worked:

114

E Problem Solving with Geometry
Suggestions For Solving Word Problems:

1. Read the problem carefully.
2. Draw a figure, diagram, or chart to help you to organize the facts.
3. Choose a meaningful variable.
4. Look for a formula.
5. Write an equation.
6. Solve the equation.
7. Check your answers back into the statement of the problem.

EXAMPLES:

Use the geometric formulas given in this section to help solve the problem.

1. A vegetable garden is in the shape of a triangle with a base of 6 feet and a height of 4 feet. Find the area of the garden.

The area of a triangle is: $A = \dfrac{1}{2}bh$

2. The length of a rectangle is 5 centimeters less than twice its width. The perimeter of the rectangle is 68 centimeters. Find the length and width of the rectangle.

Draw and label the rectangle.

Your equation is:

Length: _____   Width: _____

Note: *Perimeter- The perimeter of any polygon is the sum of the lengths of all the sides.*

EXAMPLE:

3. The perimeter of a triangle is 35 feet. The second side is 24 feet less than 3 times the first side, and the third side is 4 feet longer than the first side. Find the lengths of the sides of the triangle.

First side:

Second side:

Third side:

Your equation is:

4. Find the area of a cement walk 2.5 feet wide that surrounds a rectangular plot of ground 68 feet long and 34 feet wide.

Area of a rectangle: $A = L \cdot W$

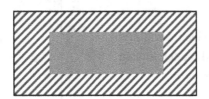

The area for the small rectangle:

The area of the large rectangle:

The area of the cement walk:

116

Name: _____   Date: _____

Instructor: _____   Section: _____

Notebook 17.1
The Rectangular Coordinate System

What makes up a rectangular coordinate system?

What is the point at which these number lines meet?

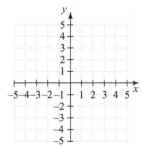

On a graph like this, in which direction is the *x*-axis positive?
Which direction is positive on the *y*-axis?
What are the four sections of the graph called?
Label them on the graph above.

True/False The order is very important when writing an ordered pair.
Write an ordered pair using an *x*-value of *x*, and a *y*-value of *y*.

What is the *x*-coordinate of an ordered pair?
What is the *y*-coordinate of an ordered pair?

What is the ordered pair for the origin?

EXAMPLE 1 Plot the points $(4, 2)$, $(3, -2)$, $(-3, 3)$, and $(-1, -4)$. Label them A, B, C and D, respectively.

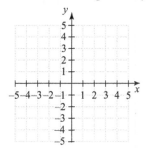

Note: If a point lies on an axis, is it in a quadrant?

117

EXAMPLE 2 Plot the points on the graph. Identify which quadrant each point lies in. Label the points *A*, *B*, *C* and *D*, respectively.

A(4, –5)
B(–5, 4)
C(3, 0)
D(2, 2)

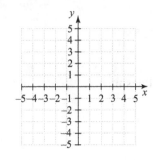

EXAMPLE 3 Find the coordinates of the indicated points. Write each point as an ordered pair. Identify which quadrant each point lies in.

A
B
C
D
E
F

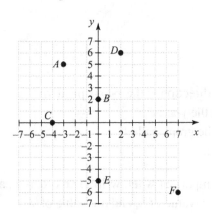

CONCEPT CHECK:

For the ordered pair (3, –4), in which direction would the coordinate –4 be plotted, and by how many units?

GUIDED EXAMPLES:

Plot the given points on the graph. Identify which quadrant each point lies in.

1. (3, 1)   2. (–2, –5)   3. (–4, 4)   4. (0, –3)

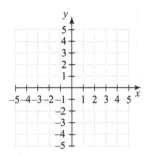

118

Name: _____   Date: _____

Instructor: _____   Section: _____

Notebook 17.2
Graphing Linear Equations by Plotting Points

What is the standard form of a linear equation?

What do A, B and C represent?

How can you tell if an ordered pair is a solution to an equation?

EXAMPLE 1 Determine whether (3, 5) is a solution to the equation $3x + 2y = 19$.

EXAMPLE 2 Determine whether (6, –4) is a solution to the equation $3x = 2y + 10$.

How many solutions does a linear equation in two variables have?

EXAMPLE 3 Find five solutions to $x + y = 10$.

10 + 0 = 10	x = 10	y = 0	is a solution	The ordered pair is (10,0)

Write the steps for finding a solution to a linear equation.
1.

2.

EXAMPLE 4 Find three solutions to $2x + y = 13$.
Substitute a value.
Solve for the other variable.
Repeat.

Where do we get the values for x?

EXAMPLE 5 Find three solutions to $y = \frac{1}{3}x - 2$.

Substitute a value.
Solve for the other variable.
Repeat.

Why did we choose these particular values (0, 3 and 6) of x?

Why use a table of values?

EXAMPLE 6 Find three solutions to $x + y = -4$.

x	y

Write the steps for graphing a linear equation by plotting points.
1.

2.

3.

EXAMPLE 7 Graph the equation $y = 2x + 1$.

Find three ordered pairs.
Plot the ordered pairs on a graph.
Draw a line.

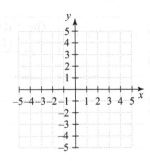

CONCEPT CHECK:
True/ False   A solution to the equation $x - y = 5$ is (9, 4).

GUIDED EXAMPLES:
Determine whether the given point is a solution to the equation.
1. $2x + 6y = 50$; (4, 7)

2. $4x - 5y = 18$; (3, – 1)

Find two solutions to the given equation.
3. $3x + y = 8$

4. $x + y = -9$

120

Notebook 17.3
Graphing Linear Equations Using Intercepts

What is an intercept?

The _____ of a line is the point where the line crosses
the _____. The ordered pair of an *x*-intercept is _____.

How do you find the *x*-intercept of a linear equation?

The _____ of a line is the point where the line crosses
the _____. The ordered pair of a *y*-intercept is _____.

How do you find the *y*-intercept?

Note: The graph of a linear equation is a _____.

EXAMPLE 1 Find the *x*-intercept and *y*-intercept of $3x - 6y = 12$.
x-intercept: *y*-intercept:

EXAMPLE 2 Find the *x*-intercept and *y*-intercept of $y = \dfrac{4}{5}x$.

x-intercept: *y*-intercept:

Note: What does it mean if the line passes through the origin?

Write the steps for graphing a linear equation using the intercepts.
1.

2.

3.

121

EXAMPLE 3 Graph $2x - y = 4$ using the intercepts.

x	y
	0
0	

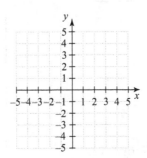

EXAMPLE 4 Graph $y = \frac{2}{3}x - 2$ using the intercepts.

x	y
	0
0	

CONCEPT CHECK:
True/False (2, 0) is a *y*-intercept.

GUIDED EXAMPLES:
Find the *x*- and *y*-intercepts of each equation.
1. $5x + 3y = 15$

2. $y = 3x - 7$

3. $4x + y = 8$

4. $y = \frac{1}{2}x + 4$

122

Notebook 17.4
Graphing Linear Equations of the form $x = a$, $y = b$, and $y = mx$

Draw a picture that shows one *x*-intercept and one *y*-intercept.

What would a line look like that has only one intercept?
Show the three cases.

Lines that pass through the _____ have only one _____.
What will the intercept will be?
Write some examples.

EXAMPLE 1 Graph $6x - 2y = 0$ using three points.

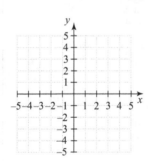

x	y

Note: How can you identify an equation of this type by looking at it?

What type of equation has a graph that is a horizontal line?
Write some examples of these equations.

What is missing from these equations?

EXAMPLES 2 & 3 Graph each equation.

$y = 4$

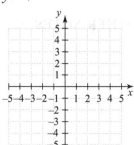

$3y + 14 = 5$

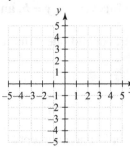

What type of equation has a graph that is a vertical line?
Write some examples of these equations.

What is missing from these equations?

EXAMPLES 4 & 5 Graph each equation.

$x = 3$

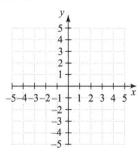

$3x + 7 = -5$

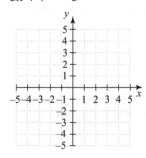

CONCEPT CHECK:
True/False $x + 5 = 0$ has only one y-intercept.

GUIDED EXAMPLES:
Graph each equation.

1. $15x - 5y = 0$

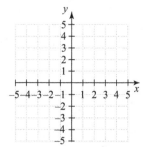

2. $y - 5 = 0$

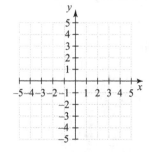

3. $x + 1 = 0$

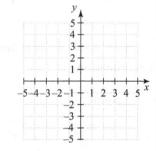

124

Name: _____   Date: _____

Instructor: _____   Section: _____

Notebook 18.1
The Slope of a Line

How can we describe the slope of a line?

What letter is used to represent slope?

How do you find the rise of a line?

How do you find the run of a line?

EXAMPLES 1 & 2 Find the slope.

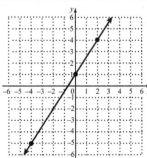   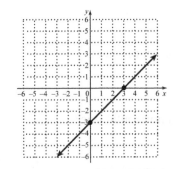

Lines with a positive slope will _____ from left to right.

EXAMPLES 3 & 4 Find the slope.

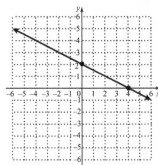   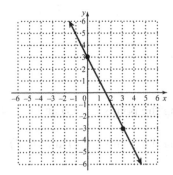

Lines with a negative slope will _____ from left to right.

Define slope.

Write the slope formula for when you know two points (x_1, y_1) and (x_2, y_2).

125

EXAMPLES 5 & 6 Find the slope of the line which contains the given points.

Use the slope formula: $m = \dfrac{y_2 - y_1}{x_2 - x_1}$.

(1, 3) and (5, 11)

(−3, −4) and (7, −9)

On a graph, what does slope measure?

If a line is steeper, what does that say about the slope?

What do you know about the slope of a horizontal line?
How do you know?

What do you know about the slope of a vertical line?
How do you know?

True/False No slope is the same as zero slope.

CONCEPT CHECK:
What is the slope of a horizontal line?

GUIDED EXAMPLES:

1. Find the slope of the line containing the points (6, 13) and (−2, 4).

2. Find the slope of the line containing the points (3, 4) and (6, 8).

3. Find the slope of the line $y = -6$.

4. Find the slope of the line $x = 5.4$.

Notebook 18.2
Slope-Intercept Form

Which intercept is the point at which a graph crosses the y-axis?

If you know two points on a line, what is the slope formula?

What is the slope-intercept form of a linear equation?

What does m represent?   What does b represent?

Caution! The slope m is only the _____.
The _____ is not included in the slope.

Write the standard form of a linear equation:

EXAMPLE 1 Find the slope and y-intercept of $y = \dfrac{2}{3}x + 5$.

Find m.
Find b.

EXAMPLE 2 Find the slope and y-intercept of $y = 4x - 6$.
Find m.
Find b.

EXAMPLE 3 Find the slope and y-intercept of $4x - 3y = 12$.
Rewrite in slope-intercept form.

Find m.

Find b.

EXAMPLE 4 Find the slope and y-intercept of $y = 3$.
Find the slope.

Find the y-intercept.

EXAMPLE 5 Find the slope and y-intercept of $x = -7$, if possible.
Find the slope.

Find the y-intercept.

EXAMPLE 6 Write the equation of a line with a slope of 2 and a y-intercept of $\left(0, \dfrac{4}{3}\right)$.

EXAMPLE 7 Write the equation of a line with a slope of –6 and a y-intercept of $(0, 0)$.

EXAMPLE 8 Write the equation of the line shown in the graph.

Find the y-intercept.
Find the slope.
Substitute.

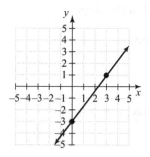

CONCEPT CHECK:

In the equation $y = mx + b$, which letter represents the slope?

GUIDED EXAMPLES:

1. Find the slope and y-intercept of the equation $y = \dfrac{6}{7}x + 3$.

2. Find the slope and y-intercept of the equation $-5x + y = 3$.

3. Write the equation of a line with a slope $\dfrac{5}{8}$ and a y-intercept of $(0, 3)$.

4. Write the equation of a line with a slope of $-\dfrac{2}{3}$ and y-intercept of $(0, 0)$.

128

Name: _____   Date: _____

Instructor: _____   Section: _____

Notebook 18.3
Graphing Lines Using the Slope and *y*-Intercept

The _____ is the point where a line crosses the *y*-axis

What are the coordinates of the *y*-intercept?

EXAMPLE 1 Find the *y*-intercept of the graph.

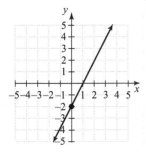

The _____ of a line that passes through two points can be found using the formula *m* = _____ .

EXAMPLE 2 Find the slope and *y*-intercept of the line in the graph.

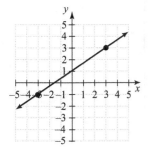

Write the steps for graphing a linear equation with slope and *y*-intercept.
1.

2.

3.

4.

The slope of a line can be described as _____ .

EXAMPLE 3 Find the slope and y-intercept of the line.

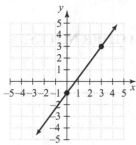

EXAMPLE 4 Graph $y = \frac{1}{2}x - 3$.

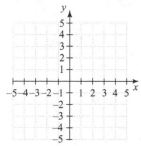

Slope, given as an integer or mixed number,
should be written as _____.
If a slope is 2, write it as _____.

How would you write a slope of $3\frac{5}{8}$?

EXAMPLE 5 Graph $y = -3x$.

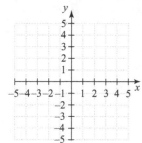

130

EXAMPLE 6 Graph $2x + 3y = 6$.

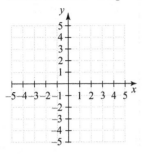

CONCEPT CHECK:

What is best described by $\dfrac{\text{rise}}{\text{run}}$?

GUIDED EXAMPLES:

Graph each equation.

1. $y = \dfrac{3}{4}x + 3$

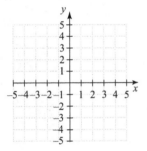

2. $y = -3x + 6$

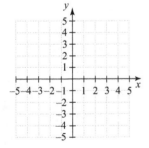

131

3. $y = x - 2$

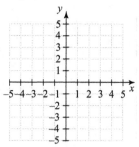

Notebook 18.4
Writing Equations of Lines Using a Point and Slope

Write the slope-intercept form of an equation of a line that has a slope m and a y-intercept of $(0, b)$.

Write the equation of the line with a slope of $-\dfrac{5}{3}$ that passes through the point $(0, -2)$.

What if the point given is not the y-intercept?

What is the point-slope form of an equation of a line?

What does m represent? What represents the point?

EXAMPLE 1 Use the point-slope form to write the equation of the line with a slope of 2 that passes through $(2, 1)$. Leave your answer in point-slope form.
  Write the point-slope equation.

  Substitute.

EXAMPLE 2 Write the equation of the line with a slope of -3 and passes through $(3, 9)$. Write your answer in slope-intercept form.
  Write the point-slope equation.

  Substitute.

  Solve for y.

EXAMPLE 3 Write the equation of the line which has a slope $\dfrac{1}{7}$ and passes through $(14, -5)$. Write your answer in slope-intercept form.
  Write the point-slope equation.

  Substitute.

  Simplify.

  Solve for y.

EXAMPLE 4 Use the point-slope form to write the equation of the line with a slope of 0 and that passes through (–16, –9). Write your answer in slope-intercept form.

Write the point-slope equation.

Substitute.

Simplify.

Solve for y.

CONCEPT CHECK:
How would $y = 2x - 3$ be written in point-slope form?

GUIDED EXAMPLES:
Write the equation of the line with the given slope and passes through the given point. Write your answer in slope-intercept form.

1. slope of 6 and passes through (–2, –1)

2. slope of $-\frac{3}{8}$ and passes through (16, 7)

3. slope of –3 and passes through (–8, –1)

Notebook 18.5
Writing Equations of Lines Using Two Points

Write the slope-intercept form of an equation of a line whose slope is m and passes through the point (x_1, y_1).

Examples
Find the slope of the line which passes through (1, 5) and (4, 11).

Write the equation of a line in slope-intercept form with a slope of 2 which passes through (1, 5).

Write the steps for writing the equation of a line given two points.
1.

2.

3.

4.

5.

EXAMPLE 1 Write the equation in slope-intercept form of the line which passes through (2, 5) and (6, 3).
Label the points as (x_1, y_1) and (x_2, y_2).

Find the slope m.

Substitute the values of x_1, y_1, and m into the point-slope form.

Solve for y to write the answer in slope-intercept form.

EXAMPLE 2 Write the equation in of the line in slope-intercept form which passes through (−1, −6) and (4,9).
Label the points as (x_1, y_1) and (x_2, y_2).

Find the slope m.

Substitute the values of x_1, y_1, and m into the point-slope form.

Solve for y to write the answer in slope-intercept form.

135

EXAMPLE 3 Write the equation of the line which passes through $(-5, 5)$ and $(0, -6)$. Write your answer in slope-intercept form.
Label the points as (x_1, y_1) and (x_2, y_2).

Find the slope m.

Substitute the values of x_1, y_1, and m into the point-slope form.

Solve for y to write the answer in slope-intercept form.

EXAMPLE 4 Write the equation of the line which passes through $(-8, 4)$ and $(-5, 0)$. Write your answer in slope-intercept form.
Label the points as (x_1, y_1) and (x_2, y_2).

Find the slope m.

Substitute the values of x_1, y_1, and m into the point-slope form.

Solve for y to write the answer in slope-intercept form.

EXAMPLE 5 Write the equation of the line shown on the graph. Write your answer in slope-intercept form.

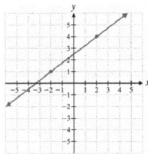

CONCEPT CHECK:
True/False In order to write the equation of a line given two points, one of the points must have an x- or y-coordinate of 0.

GUIDED EXAMPLES:
Write the equation of the line which passes through each pair of points. Write your answer in slope-intercept form.
1. $(6, 5)$ and $(8, 9)$

2. $(3, -5)$ and $(12, 1)$

3. $(2, -3)$ and $(7, -11)$

4. $(-22, -1)$ and $(11, 20)$

136

Notebook 18.6
Writing Equations of Parallel and Perpendicular Lines

What are parallel lines?

Parallel lines have _____ slopes but different _____.

What is the symbol for parallel lines?

What is the slope-intercept form of an equation of a line?

What does *m* represent? What represents the *y*-intercept?

EXAMPLE 1 Find the slope of a line parallel to $y = \frac{3}{4}x + 2$.

Find the slope of the line.

Find the slope of a parallel line.

What are perpendicular lines?
Draw lines that are perpendicular.

The slopes of perpendicular lines are _____.
What does that mean?
What is the symbol for perpendicular lines?

EXAMPLE 2 Find the slope of a line perpendicular to $6x + 2y = 9$.
Find the slope of the line.

Find the slope of a perpendicular line.

EXAMPLE 3 Find the slope of a line parallel to the given line and the slope of
a line perpendicular to the given line. $-3x + 5y = -11$
Find the slope of the line.

Find the slope of a parallel line.

Find the slope of a perpendicular line.

EXAMPLE 4 Determine if the lines are parallel, perpendicular, or neither.
$y = 2x + 3$
$-8x + 4y = -4$

137

EXAMPLE 5 Determine if the lines are parallel, perpendicular, or neither.

$x - 4y = 0$

$y = \dfrac{-1}{3}x - 1$

What is the equation of a horizontal line?
What is the slope of a horizontal line?

What is the equation of a vertical line?
What is the slope of a vertical line?

Write the formula for finding slope of a line containing two points.

EXAMPLE 6 Find the slope of the line containing the points (2, 6) and (4,6). Then find the slope of a line parallel to this line and the slope of a line perpendicular to this line.

Write the point-slope form of an equation.

EXAMPLE 7 Find the equation of a line perpendicular to $y = \dfrac{3}{5}x + 8$ that passes through the point (3, –1). Write the answer in slope-intercept form.

CONCEPT CHECK:
True/False The slopes of perpendicular lines are negative reciprocals.

GUIDED EXAMPLES:
1. Find the slope of a line parallel and perpendicular to the given line.

   $y = \dfrac{5}{2}x + 16$

2. Determine if the given lines are parallel, perpendicular, or neither.
   $2y = 6x + 8$
   $9x - 3y = -3$

3. Find the slope of a line parallel and perpendicular to $7x - 3y = -18$.

4. Find the equation of a line perpendicular to $4x - 2y = -12$ that passes through the point (−8, 6). Write the answer in slope-intercept form.

138

Name: _____   Date: _____

Instructor: _____   Section: _____

Notebook 19.1
Relations and Functions

OTHER NOTES

What are three ways that a linear equation in two variables can be represented?

x is called the _____ variable and
y is called the _____ variable.

What is a relation?

What makes up the domain of the relation?
What makes up the range of the relation?

EXAMPLE 1 State the domain and range of the relation.
$\{(5, 7), (9, 11), (10, 7), 12, 14)\}$
domain:

range:

What is a function?

No two _____ ordered pairs can have the same

_____ _____.

EXAMPLES 2 & 3 Determine whether each relation is a function.
$\{(3, 9), (4, 16), (5, 9), (6, 36)\}$

$\{(7, 8), (9, 10), (12, 13), (7, 14)\}$

EXAMPLES 4 – 6 Determine whether each relation is a function.
$y = 3x - 5$

$y = |x|$

$y^2 = x$

EXAMPLE 7 Keith makes $10 per hour at his after-school job.
Determine whether the relation between the number of hours he works, x, and his earnings, y, is a function. If it is a function, identify the domain and range.

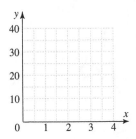

domain:

range:

CONCEPT CHECK: What is a relation for which every x-value in the domain has one and only one y-value?

GUIDED EXAMPLES:
1. State the domain and range of the relation. $\{(0, 0), (1, 1), (2, 2), (3, 3)\}$

2. Determine whether the relation is a function. $\{(6, 7), (7, 8), (8, 7)\}$

3. Determine whether the relation is a function. $y = |-3x| + 1$

4. Each month, Ashley pays $40 for her cell phone bill plus $0.05 for each text message that she sends. Determine whether the relation between the number of text messages she sends, x, and the amount of her cell phone bill, y, is a function. If it is a function, identify the domain and range.

Notebook 19.3
Function Notation

If the name of a function is f and the variable is x, what would the function notation be?

How do you read $f(x)$?

EXAMPLES 1 & 2 Use function notation to rewrite the following functions using the given function names.
$y = 9x - 2$, function name f

$y = -16t^2 + 10$, function name h

Note: The variable that is inside the parentheses makes up the _____.
Caution! $f(x)$ does NOT mean _____.

What is the domain of a function?
What is the range?

EXAMPLE 3 Determine the domain and the range of the function.
$f(x) = -4x + 10$

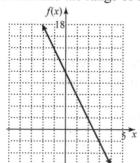

domain:

range:

EXAMPLES 4 & 5 Determine the domain and the range of the function.
$g(x) = x^2 - 4$

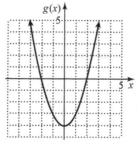

domain:

range:

141

$h(t) = \sqrt{t}.$

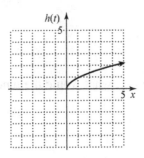

domain:

range:

CONCEPT CHECK:
How can we know that the domain of $f(x) = 3x - 2$ is all real numbers?

GUIDED EXAMPLES:
1. Use function notation to rewrite the function using the given function name.
   $y = 3x + 7$, function name of g

2. Determine the domain and range of the function based on its graph.
   $f(x) = 2x - 5$

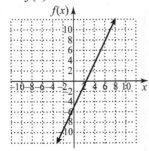

3. Determine the domain and range of the function based on its graph.
   $f(x) = |x|$

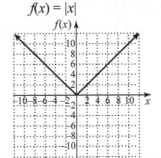

4. Determine the domain and range of the function based on its graph.

   $p(x) = 2x^3 - 6x^2 + 1$

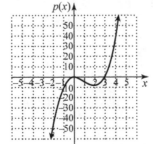

142

Name: _____   Date: _____

Instructor: _____   Section: _____

Notebook 19.4
Evaluating Functions

What is the procedure for evaluating a function at a certain value?

EXAMPLES 1 & 2 If $f(x) = x + 8$, find the following.

$f(2)$

$f(-6)$

Remember:

$-3^2 =$

$(-3)^2$

$-(-3)^2$

EXAMPLES 3 – 5 If $f(x) = 2x^2 - 4$, find each of the following.

$f(5)$

$f(-3)$

$f(0)$

EXAMPLE 6 The approximate length of a man's femur (thigh bone) is given by the function $f(x) = 0.5x - 17$, where x is the height of the man in inches. Find the approximate length of the femur of a man who is 70 inches tall.

CONCEPT CHECK:

If $f(4) = 6$, what is the ordered pair that is on the graph of the function?

GUIDED EXAMPLES:

1. If $f(x) = 10x - 5$, find $f(-2)$.

2. If $f(x) = x^2 - 2x$, find $f(-2)$.

3. The height of an object dropped from a 100-foot building is given by $h(t) = -16t^2 + 100$, where t is the time after the object is dropped in seconds. Find the height of an object 2 seconds after it is dropped from 100 feet.

144

Notebook 20.1
Introduction to Systems of Linear Equations

In order to be a solution to a system, the ordered pair must make each equation in the system ____.

When observing the graphs of these equations, where is the solution?

What is a system of linear equations?

What is a solution to a system of equations?

Every solution to a system of equations has two parts, which are written together as an ordered pair. What are the two parts?

EXAMPLE 1 Determine whether $(3, -2)$ is a solution to the following system of equations.

$$x + 3y = -3$$
$$4x + 3y = 6$$

EXAMPLE 2 Determine whether $(4, 3)$ is a solution to the following system of equations.

$$7x - 4y = 16$$
$$5x + 2y = 24$$

EXAMPLE 3 Determine whether $(-9, -7)$ is a solution to the following system of equations.

$$3y = 2x - 3$$
$$y = x - 5$$

EXAMPLE 4 Determine whether $\left(\dfrac{4}{3}, \dfrac{1}{6}\right)$ is a solution to the following system of equations.

$$2y = 1 - \dfrac{1}{2}x$$
$$3x = 2 + 12y$$

EXAMPLE 5 Determine whether (7, 6) is a solution to the following system of equations.

$$0.3x + 0.2y = 2.7$$
$$9x - 3y = 4$$

CONCEPT CHECK:
How do you check the solution for a system of equations?

GUIDED EXAMPLES:
1. Determine whether (–6, –11) is a solution to the system.

$$3x - 2y = 4$$
$$-9x + 3y = 21$$

2. Determine whether (5, 1) is a solution to the system.

$$x + 8y = 12$$
$$-3x - y = -16$$

3. Determine whether (13, –2) is a solution to the system.

$$0.2x + 1.5y = -0.4$$
$$3x - 2y = 35$$

4. Determine whether $\left(-\dfrac{2}{3}, -\dfrac{3}{5}\right)$ is a solution to the following system of equations.

$$6x = 5y - 1$$
$$\dfrac{5}{3}y = -2x + 1$$

146

Solving Systems of Equations by Graphing

To solve a system of equations by graphing:
Graph both equations on the same coordinate plane.
The solution to the system is the _____ where the lines _____.
If the lines do not intersect, there is _____.
If both equations form the same line there is _____.

EXAMPLE Solve by graphing.

$y = x - 3$

$3x + 2y = 4$

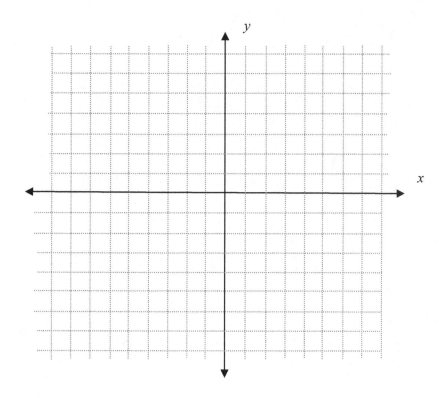

148

Notebook 20.3
Solving by the Substitution Method

When solving a system of equations using the graphing method, the solution is the _____.

This could be difficult if the solution is a _____.

Thus, the need for the substitution method.
Write the steps for solving systems using substitution.
1. Choose _____ equation and _____ for either variable in terms of the other. _____ this equation.

2. _____ the expression from step 1 into the _____ equations.

3. _____ this equation.

4. _____ this value in place of the _____ into either of the _____ equations to obtain a value for the second _____. _____ this equation.

5. Write the values for both variables in an _____.

6. _____ the solution in _____ equations.
Note: What happens if, after step 3, you get an equation with no variables?
A true result means …

A false result means…

EXAMPLE 1 Solve the system of equations by substitution. Then check.
$$4x + 3y = 50$$
$$y = 2x$$

EXAMPLE 2 Solve the system of equations by substitution. Then check.
$$y = x - 5$$
$$3x - 2y = 17$$

EXAMPLE 3 Solve the system of equations by substitution. Then check.
$$-4x + 3y = 10$$
$$-6x + y = 1$$

Note: Again, what happens if you get an equation with no variables and
the result is true?
the result is false?

EXAMPLE 4 Solve the system of equations by substitution. Then check.
$$4x - 24y = 40$$
$$x - 6y = 10$$

EXAMPLE 5 Solve the system of equations by substitution. Then check.
$$x + 3y = 5$$
$$4x + 12y = 40$$

$$=$$

CONCEPT CHECK:
After a system of equations has been solved, what would a result of 2 = 0 mean?

GUIDED EXAMPLES:
Solve the system of equations by substitution. Then check.

1. $3x + 2y = 15$
   $y = 6x$

2. $2x + y = -1$
   $3x + 3y = 15$

3. $y = 3x + 1$
   $6x - 2y = -2$

4. $y = -2x + 3$
   $2x + y = 6$

150

Notebook 20.4
Solving by the Elimination Method

A _____ is a set of two or more equations with the same variables.

The _____ to a system of equations is the _____ that is a solution to every equation in the system.

The solution to a system of equations has 2 parts, which are written together as an _____.

What are opposite numbers?

EXAMPLE 1 Solve the system of equations. Then check.
$$7x - 3y = 1$$
$$5x + 3y = 11$$

Write the steps for solving systems by elimination.
1. Arrange each equation in the form _____.

2. If necessary, _____ one or both _____ by the appropriate number so that the _____ of either variable are _____.

3. _____ the two equations so that the variable is eliminated.

4. _____ the resulting _____.

5. _____ this value into either of the _____ _____ and _____ to find the value of the other variable.

6. _____ the solution as an _____.

7. _____ the solution in both of the _____.

Note: What happens if, after step 3, you get an equation with no variables?
A true result means …
A false result means…

EXAMPLE 2 Solve the system of equations by elimination. Then check.
$$3x + 7y = 22$$
$$3x - 7y = 3$$

EXAMPLE 3 Solve the system of equations by elimination. Then check.

$$4x - 10y = -44$$
$$9x - 5y = 6$$

Note: An easy way to know what numbers to multiply each equation is to: _____ which _____ you want to _____; _____ each equation by the _____ of that variable term in the _____ equation.

Caution! Make sure you multiply _____ sides of the equation by the number.

EXAMPLE 4 Solve the system of equations by elimination. Then check.

$$4x + 3y = -5$$
$$7x + 2y = 14$$

EXAMPLE 5 Solve the system of equations by elimination. Then check.

$$3x + 2y = 18$$
$$-3x - 2y = 14$$

EXAMPLE 6 Solve the system of equations by elimination. Then check.

$$9x - 6y = 24$$
$$3x - 2y = 8$$

CONCEPT CHECK:
What is the first step in solving a system of equations using elimination?

GUIDED EXAMPLES:
Solve the system of equations by elimination. Then check.

1.　$8x + 4y = -4$
　　$-8x - 7y = -11$

2.　$5x + 4y = 96$
　　$9x - 3y = 81$

3.　$6x + 9y = 24$
　　$4x + 6y = 15$

4.　$12x - 5y = -7$
　　$4x + 2y = 5$

152

Notebook 20.6
Applications of Systems of Linear Equations

Write the steps for solving applications with a system of equations:
1.

2.

3.

4.

5.

6.

EXAMPLE 1 A movie theater sells tickets for $10 and bags of popcorn for $3. In a single Saturday night, the theater had $2375 in sales. The theater owner found that if he raised ticket prices to $11, raised popcorn prices to $4, and sold the same number of tickets and popcorn, the theater would make $2700. How many tickets were sold? How many bags of popcorn were sold?
Define the variables.
Write a system of equations.
Solve.

EXAMPLE 2 A boat travels 20 miles upstream, against the current, in 4 hours. The return trip, 20 miles downstream, with the current, only takes 2 hours. Find the speed of the boat in still water and the speed of the current.
Let r = the speed of the boat in still water, and c = the speed of the river current.
Note: Distance = _____ × _____

	Distance	Rate	Time	Equation
Upstream				
Downstream				

EXAMPLE 3 An electronics company makes two types of switches. Type A takes 4 minutes to make and requires $3 worth of materials. Type B takes 5 minutes to make and requires $5 worth of materials. In the latest production batch, it took 35 hours to make these switches, and the materials cost $1900. How many of each type of switch were made?

Stop watching video after Example 3.

CONCEPT CHECK:

What is the first step in solving applications involving systems of linear equations?

GUIDED EXAMPLES:

1. Concert tickets bought in advance cost $5, but at the door they are $6. The ticket sales came to $4540. The concert promoter raises tickets for the next show to $7 in advance and $9 at the door. If the same number of people attend the next concert, the ticket sales will total $6560. Find how many tickets were sold in advance and how many were bought at the door.

2. A boat travels 105 km downstream in 5 hours. The return trip upstream takes 7 hours. Find the speed of the boat in still water and the speed of the current.

3. A furniture company makes large and small chairs. A small chair takes 30 minutes of machine time and 75 minutes of labor to build. A large chair takes 40 minutes of machine time and 80 minutes of labor to build. The company has 57 hours of labor time and 26 hours of machine time available each day. How many of each type of chair is built in a day?

154

Notebook 21.1
Introduction to Polynomials

A _____ is any number, variable, or product of numbers and/or variables.

A _____ is a number that is multiplied by a variable.

Terms that have the same variable(s) raised to the same exponent(s) are called

_____.

Reminder: How do you combine like terms?

What is a polynomial in the variable x?

What does it mean to write a polynomial in descending order?

What is the degree of a term?

What if there is more than one variable, then how do you get the degree of the term?

The degree of any constant (numerical) term is _____.

EXAMPLES 1–3 Find the degree of each term.
$7x^3$

$4ab^2$

10

What is the degree of a polynomial?

EXAMPLES 4 & 5 For each polynomial, find the degree of each term. Then find the degree of the polynomial.
$5x^3 + 8x^2 - 20x - 2$

$6xy - 4x^2y + 2xy^3$

There are special names for polynomials with _____, _____, or _____ terms.

A _____ is a polynomial with exactly _____ term. Example:

A _____ is a polynomial with exactly _____ terms. Example:

A _____ is a polynomial with exactly _____ terms. Example:

EXAMPLES 6–8 State the degree of the polynomial, and state whether each polynomial is a monomial, a binomial, or a trinomial.

$5x + 3x^3$

$-7a^5b^2$

$8x^4 - 9x - 15$

What is the procedure for evaluating a polynomial?

EXAMPLE 9 Evaluate the polynomial $P(x) = 2x^2 - 6x + 7$ at $x = -2$.

EXAMPLE 10 The height of an object dropped from a 200 ft building is given by the polynomial $h(t) = -16t^2 + 200$, where t is the time after the object is dropped in seconds. Find the height of an object 3 seconds after it is dropped from 200 feet.

CONCEPT CHECK:
True/False The polynomial $5x^4 + 6x$ has a degree of 4.

GUIDED EXAMPLES:

1. Find the degree of each term. $3x^4$ and $2xy^2$

2. Find the degree of the polynomial. $7xy^2 - 2x^2y^2 + 5y$

3. Evaluate the polynomial. $P(x) = -4x^3 + 2x^2 - x + 5$

4. The concentration C, in parts per million, of a certain antibiotic in the bloodstream after t hours is given by the polynomial $C(t) = -0.05t^2 + 2t + 2$. Find the concentration after 4 hours.

156

Notebook 21.2
Addition of Polynomials

Terms that have the same variable(s) raised to the same exponent(s) are called

_____.

Like terms can be combined by _____ or _____
the coefficients of the terms. Example.

What is the rule for adding polynomials?

EXAMPLE 1 Add. $(x + y) + (2x + 6y)$

EXAMPLE 2 Add. $(5x^2 - 6x - 12) + (-3x^2 - 9x + 5)$

EXAMPLE 3 Add. $(7x^2 + 8x + 9) + (13x^2 - 10x + 5)$

EXAMPLE 4 Add. $(1.2x^3 - 5.6x^2 + 5) + (-3.4x^3 - 1.2x^2 + 4.5x - 7)$

EXAMPLE 5 Add. $\left(\frac{1}{2}x^2 - 6x + \frac{1}{3}\right) + \left(2x - \frac{1}{2} + \frac{1}{5}x^3\right)$

EXAMPLE 6 Add. $(6x^2 - x + 4) + (10x - 8x^2 - 3)$

CONCEPT CHECK:

What is the simplest form of $5.1x^2 - 2x^2 + 3x + 0.5x - 12 + 5$?

GUIDED EXAMPLES:

Add each of the following.

1. $(-8x^3 + 3x^2 + 6) + (2x^3 - 7x^2 - 3)$

2. $(12x^2 - 8x - 11) + (-7x^2 + 6x - 13)$

3. $(3.5x^3 - 0.02x^2 + 1.56x - 3.5) + (-0.08x^2 - 1.98x + 4)$

4. $\left(-\dfrac{1}{3}x^2 - 6x - \dfrac{1}{12}\right) + \left(5x + \dfrac{1}{4}x^2 - \dfrac{1}{3}\right)$

158

Name: _____   Date: _____

Instructor: _____   Section: _____

Notebook 21.3
Subtraction of Polynomials

To add two polynomials, _____.

Subtraction can be defined as _____.

What is the procedure for subtracting polynomials?

EXAMPLE 1 Subtract. $(2x + 3) - (x - 5)$
Change the sign of each term in the second polynomial.

Add by combining like terms.

EXAMPLE 2 Subtract. $(-2x^3 + 7x^2 - 3x - 1) - (-6x^3 - 9x^2 - x + 4)$

EXAMPLE 3 Subtract. $(-3x^4 + 5x^2 + 2) - (6x^3 - 10x^2 + 2x - 1)$

EXAMPLE 4 Subtract. $(0.7x^3 - 1.2x - 4.8) - (1.6x^3 + 9.4x - 6.5)$

Caution! Use extra care in determining which terms are _____
when polynomials contain more than one variable.

EXAMPLE 5 Subtract. $(-6x^2y - 3xy + 7xy^2) - (5x^2y - 8xy - 15x^2y^2)$

CONCEPT CHECK:

What is the first step when subtracting polynomials?

GUIDED EXAMPLES:

Simplify each of the following.

1. $(-8x^2 + 3x - 7) - (5x^2 - 6x + 2)$

2. $(12x^5 - 3x^3 + 8x - 6) - (-4x^5 + 13x^4 + 5x^2 - 10x + 4)$

3. $(7.2x^2 - 1.4x - 4.5) - (2.3x - 0.8x^2 + 3.6)$

4. $(a^3 - 7a^2b + 3ab^2 - 2b^3) - (2a^3 + 4ab - 6b^3)$

160

Name: _____   Date: _____

Instructor: _____   Section: _____

Notebook 21.4
Product Rule for Exponents

An _____ is used as a shortcut for repeated multiplication.
The number being multiplied is the _____.
The number of times the base is used as a factor is the _____.

What is an exponential expression?

What happens when we multiply exponential expressions? Give examples.

What happens to the base?
What happens to the exponent?

What does the product rule for exponents say about multiplying exponential expressions that have like bases?

EXAMPLES 1–3 Multiply.
$x^3 \cdot x^6$

$y \cdot y^5$

$x^3 \cdot x \cdot x^6$

Caution! What do you do if the variable does not have a written exponent?

Caution! The product rule for exponents applies only to expressions that
_____.

EXAMPLES 4–6 Simplify, if possible.
Write your answer using exponential notation..
$y^5 \cdot y^{11}$

$2^3 \cdot 2^5$

$x^6 \cdot y^8$

How do you multiply exponential expression with coefficients?

161

EXAMPLES 7–9 Multiply.
Write your answer using exponential notation.

$(3a)^2(3a)^4$

$(5x^3)(x^6)$

$(-6x)(-4x^5)$

What do you do in cases where the problems involve more than one variable or more than two factors?

EXAMPLE 10 Multiply. $(5ab)\left(-\dfrac{1}{3}a\right)(9b^2)$

CONCEPT CHECK:
The product rule can be applied when _____ exponential expressions with like bases. (Fill in which multiplying, dividing or adding.)

GUIDED EXAMPLES:
Multiply each of the following.
1. Multiply. $w^{10} \cdot w$

2. Simplify by the product rule, if possible. $(4x)^3(4x)^7$

3. Multiply. $(-4x^3)(-5x^2)$

4. Multiply. $(2xy)\left(-\dfrac{1}{4}x^2y^2\right)(6xy^3)$

Notebook 21.5
Power Rule for Exponents

An exponent is used as a shortcut for _____.
The base is the number being _____.
The exponent is the number of times the base is used as a _____.

An _____ is a variable or a number raised to
an exponent.

To multiply two exponential expressions that have _____,
_____ the base and _____ the exponents.
Example:

What does the power rule for exponents say about raising a product to a power?

EXAMPLES 1–3 Simplify. Write your answer using exponential notation.
$(x^3)^5$

$(2^7)^3$

$(y^2)^4$

How do you raise a product to a power?
Example:

EXAMPLES 4–6 Simplify.
$(ab)^8$

$(3x)^4$

$(-2x^2)^3$

How do you raise a fractional expression (quotient) to a power?
Example:

EXAMPLES 7 & 8 Simplify. Write your answer using exponential notation.

$$\left(\frac{x}{y}\right)^5$$

$$\left(\frac{3}{w}\right)^4$$

Caution! As long as you use the rules _____, you can apply them in _____ order. Be sure to take care to determine the correct _____ of the expression, especially if there is a _____.

EXAMPLE 9 Simplify. $\left(\dfrac{-3x^2z^0}{y^3}\right)^4$

CONCEPT CHECK:

How would the z variable in $(-3x^2yz^0)^3$ be simplified?

GUIDED EXAMPLES:

1. Simplify. Write your answer using exponential notation. $(y^3)^7$

2. Simplify. $(2y^4)^2$

3. Simplify. $\left(-\dfrac{7a}{b}\right)^2$

4. Simplify. $\left(\dfrac{2y^0z^2}{4x^3}\right)^5$

164

Name: _____   Date: _____

Instructor: _____   Section: _____

Notebook 22.1
Multiplying by a Monomial

For all real numbers a, b, and c, $a(b + c) = $ _____.

To multiply two exponential expressions that have _____,
_____ the base and _____ the exponents.

In symbols, this looks like …

What does the power rule for exponents say about raising a product to a power?

Give some examples of monomials.

A _____ is a polynomial with exactly one term.

What is the rule for multiplying a monomial by a polynomial?

EXAMPLE 1 Multiply. $3x^2(5x - 2)$

EXAMPLE 2 Multiply. $2x(x^2 + 3x - 1)$

EXAMPLE 3 Multiply. $-6xy(x^3 + 2x^2y - y^2)$

EXAMPLE 4 Multiply. $3a(2a^3 - 3a^2 + 7a)$

EXAMPLE 5 Multiply. $(2x^2 - 3x + 8)(-7x)$
Rewrite using Commutative Property.

Note: Why did we change the order here?

CONCEPT CHECK:
Use the Distributive Property to simplify $3(x - 4)$.

GUIDED EXAMPLES:
1. Multiply. $4x^3(-2x^2 + 3x)$

2. Multiply. $3x(x^2 + 2x - 4)$

3. Multiply. $-2xy^2(x^2 - 5xy - 3y^2)$

4. Multiply. $(x^3 - 2x + 6)(-2x)$

166

Notebook 22.2
Multiplying Binomials

A _____ is a polynomial with exactly two terms.
Give some examples of binomials.

Write the steps for multiplying binomials.
1.

2.

3.

EXAMPLE 1 Multiply. $(3x + 1)(x + 4)$

EXAMPLE 2 Multiply. $(7x - 4)(6x + 3)$

What happens if one or more of the binomials involve subtraction?

EXAMPLE 3 Multiply. $(4x - 9y)(8x - 3)$

Does the process of multiplication change if there is more than one variable in a binomial?

How is the FOIL method used in multiplying binomials?
F:
O:
I:
L:

167

Can the FOIL method be used to multiply any binomials?
If not, which ones?

EXAMPLE 4 Multiply using the FOIL method. $(x + 3)(x + 5)$
First:
Outer:
Inner:
Last:

EXAMPLE 5 Multiply using the FOIL method. $(2x + 1)(3x + 4)$
First:
Outer:
Inner:
Last:

EXAMPLE 6 Multiply using the FOIL method. $(-2 + 7x)(-9x + 5)$
First:
Outer:
Inner:
Last:

CONCEPT CHECK:
Which of the following is a binomial?. $x^2 + 7$ or $3a^2 + 4a - 5$

GUIDED EXAMPLES:
1. Multiply. $(x + 2)(5x + 8)$

2. Multiply. $(2x - 15y)(7x - 2)$

3. Multiply using the FOIL method. $(x^2 + 2)(x^2 + 9)$

4. Multiply using the FOIL method. $(3x^2 - 2)(-4x^2 + 5)$

168

Name: _____   Date: _____

Instructor: _____   Section: _____

Notebook 22.3
Multiplying Polynomials

The _____ can be used to multiply a polynomial by a monomial.
Ex. Multiply. $3x(4x^2 + x - 2)$

The Distributive Property can also be used to multiply two _____.
Ex. Multiply. $(2x + 3)(4x + 5)$

What does it mean if a polynomial in x is written in descending order?

Write the steps for multiplying polynomials.
1.

2.

3.

4.

EXAMPLE 1 Multiply. $(x + 4)(3x^2 + x + 2)$
Multiply each term in the first
polynomial by every term in the
second polynomial.

Write the sum.
Combine like terms.
Descending order.

EXAMPLE 2 Multiply. $(3x - 1)(6x^2 - 5x + 8)$

EXAMPLE 3 Multiply. $(5x^5 + 2x^2 + 7)(x^4 + x)$

169

EXAMPLE 4 Multiply. $(4x^2 + 9x + 7)(2x^2 - 6x - 5)$

Integers, as well as polynomials, can be multiplied _____.
Multiply $(x^2 + 3x + 8)(2x^2 + 4x - 5)$ vertically.

How do you multiply three or more polynomials?

EXAMPLE 5 Multiply. $(x + 1)(x + 2)(x + 3)$

CONCEPT CHECK: Is $3x^2 + 9x^3 - 2x^4 + 7x^5$ written in descending order?

GUIDED EXAMPLES:

1. Multiply. $(9x + 5)(x^2 + 7x - 3)$

2. Multiply. $(3x^2 - 4x - 6)(2x - 3)$

3. Multiply. $(x^2 + 3x + 4)(2x^2 - x - 7)$

4. Multiply. $(3x + 2)(5x - 7)(x + 1)$

Name: _____   Date: _____

Instructor: _____   Section: _____

Notebook 22.4
Multiplying the Sum and Difference of Two Terms

To multiply two binomials, multiply each term in the _____ binomial by each term in the _____ binomial, or use _____.

Multiply $(x + 3)(x - 3)$.

EXAMPLE 1 Multiply. $(5x + 4)(5x - 4)$

What are some observations from the pattern?

What is the rule for multiplying binomials for a sum and a difference?

EXAMPLES 2 & 3 Multiply.
$(x + 5)(x - 5)$

$(7a - 8)(7a + 8)$

EXAMPLES 4 & 5 Multiply.
$(2x^2 + 3y)(2x^2 - 3y)$

$\left(\frac{1}{4}x - \frac{2}{3}\right)\left(\frac{1}{4}x + \frac{2}{3}\right)$

Show why this formula for multiplying a sum and difference works.

Use formula (shortcut) $(a - b)(a + b) =$

Use FOIL $(a - b)(a + b) =$

CONCEPT CHECK: Write the formula for multiplying the sum and difference of two terms.

GUIDED EXAMPLES:

1. Multiply. $(x - 2)(x + 2)$

2. Multiply. $(6x + 1)(6x - 1)$

3. Multiply. $(7x^3 + 12y)(7x^3 - 12y)$

4. Multiply. $(xy - 7)(xy + 7)$

172

Notebook 22.5
Squaring Binomials

To multiply two binomials, multiply each term in the _____ binomial by each term in the _____ binomial, or use _____.

Multiply $(x + 7)(x + 7)$.

Caution! $(x + 7)^2 = (x + 7)(x + 7)$
$(x + 7)^2$ does not mean $x^2 + 7^2$

EXAMPLE 1 Simplify.
$(2x - 3)^2$

Write as a multiplication problem.
Multiply the binomials.
Simplify.

What are some observations from the pattern?

What are the rules for squaring a binomial?
$(a + b)^2 =$
$(a - b)^2 =$

EXAMPLE 2 Simplify.
$(3x + 5)^2$

EXAMPLES 3 & 4 Simplify.

$(x - 5)^2$

$(2x^2 + 3y)^2$

EXAMPLE 5 Simplify.

$\left(\dfrac{1}{4}x - \dfrac{2}{3}\right)^2$

CONCEPT CHECK: Write the formula for squaring a binomial.

GUIDED EXAMPLES:

1. Multiply. $(3x + 11)^2$

2. Multiply. $(8x^3 + 9)^2$

3. Multiply. $(6x - 1)^2$

4. Multiply. $\left(\dfrac{3}{8}y - \dfrac{1}{10}\right)^2$

174

Notebook 23.1
The Quotient Rule

To simplify a fraction using the prime factors method,
1. Write the _____ and _____ as the
   product of _____-.
2. Divide by _____ in the numerator and denominator.
3. Multiply the remaining _____ to get simplest form.

Example. Simplify using the prime factors method.

$\dfrac{64}{16}$

Why do you need to review simplifying fractions?

EXAMPLE 1 Simplify using the prime factors method.

$\dfrac{x^6}{x^4}$

EXAMPLE 2 Simplify using the prime factors method.

$\dfrac{25x^6}{10x^3}$

What does the Quotient Rule say?
To _____ like bases, _____ the base and _____
the exponents. In symbols, …

EXAMPLES 3–5 Simplify.

$\dfrac{x^3}{x^2}$

$\dfrac{42y^5}{18y^3}$

$-\dfrac{16s^6}{32s^2}$

EXAMPLE 6 Simplify using the quotient rule.

$\dfrac{7^{10}}{7^4}$

Caution! The _____ does not change, only the _____ changes.

175

EXAMPLE 7 Simplify using the quotient rule.

$$\frac{y^5}{y^5}$$

Remember, any non-zero number divided by itself is _____.

What does the "Zero as an Exponent Property" say?

Note: What about 0^0?

EXAMPLES 8–10 Evaluate. Assume all variables represent nonnegative numbers.

$$\frac{8^5}{8^5}$$

$$\frac{(ax)^4}{(ax)^4}$$

$$\frac{5x^3}{x^3}$$

CONCEPT CHECK: Apply the quotient rule to $\dfrac{5x^4y^2}{x^2y}$.

GUIDED EXAMPLES:

1. Simplify by the prime factors method. $\dfrac{x^8}{x^3}$

2. Simplify by the prime factors method. $-\dfrac{64n^6}{12n^4}$

3. Simplify using the quotient rule. $\dfrac{p^{13}}{p^8}$

4. Evaluate using the quotient rule. $\dfrac{12x^4}{4x^4}$

176

Notebook 23.2
Integer Exponents

Simplify using the prime factors method and the quotient rule.

$$\frac{x^3}{x^8} =$$ $$\frac{x^3}{x^8} =$$

What does a negative exponent mean?

Note: A negative exponent means _____.
It does not affect _____.

EXAMPLES 1–3 Simplify. Write your answer with positive exponents.

$$z^{-6}$$

$$\frac{x^3}{x^7}$$

$$(x^{-5})(x^3)$$

Remember the sign rules for raising a negative base to a power.

$$(-a)^{\text{even}} =$$ $$(-a)^{\text{odd}} =$$

$$(-2)^2 =$$ $$(-2)^3 =$$

EXAMPLES 4–6 Simplify. Write your answers with positive exponents.

$$2^{-5}$$

$$-5^{-2}$$

$$(-3)^{-3}$$

Assuming that m and n are real numbers, $x \neq 0$, and $y \neq 0$, what are the two properties of negative exponents?

$$\frac{1}{x^{-n}} =$$ $$\frac{x^{-m}}{y^{-n}}$$

EXAMPLES 7–9 Simplify. Write your answers with positive exponents.

$$\frac{1}{x^{-8}}$$

$$\frac{x^{-4}}{y^{-2}}$$

$$\frac{16^{-8}}{23^{-7}}$$

How do you know if an exponential expression is simplified?

all _____ have been removed,

all _____ are positive, and

all _____ are simplified.

What are the three properties for the Power Rules?

EXAMPLE 10 Simplify. Write your answer with positive exponents.

$(3x^{-4}y^2)^{-3}$

What does the Product Rule state?

EXAMPLE 11 Simplify. Write your answer with positive exponents.

$\dfrac{x^2y^{-4}}{x^{-5}y^3}$

What does Quotient Rule say?

EXAMPLE 11 Simplify. Write your answer with positive exponents.

$\dfrac{(4x)^{-2}5y^{-7}}{x^6y^{-4}}$

CONCEPT CHECK: Write $(ab)^2$ in simplest form.

GUIDED EXAMPLES:

Simplify. Write your answer with positive exponents.

1. m^{-16}

2. $\dfrac{a^{-2}}{a^5}$

Evaluate. Write your answers with positive exponents.

3. $(4a^3b^{-7})^{-4}$

4. $\dfrac{-7a^{-7}(6b^4)^{-2}}{a^{-2}b^{-11}}$

Notebook 23.4
Dividing a Polynomial by a Monomial

EXAMPLES 1 & 2 Simplify.

$$\frac{3}{5} + \frac{1}{5}$$

$$\frac{6x + 4}{2}$$

What is the rule for dividing a polynomial by a monomial?

EXAMPLE 3 Divide.
$$\frac{15x^5 + 10x^4 + 25x^3}{5x^2}$$
Split the division problem up.
Divide each term.
Write the sum of the results.

EXAMPLE 4 Divide.
$$\frac{63x^7 - 35x^6 - 49x^5}{-7x^3}$$

EXAMPLE 5 Divide.
$(36x^3 - 18x^2 + 9x) \div (9x)$

EXAMPLE 6 Divide.
$$\frac{16x^4 - 9x^3 + 24x^2}{12x^2}$$

179

EXAMPLE 7 Divide.

$$\frac{24x^3 + 16x^2 - 56x}{8x^2}$$

CONCEPT CHECK:

The final division for $\dfrac{50x^8 - 30x^5 + 20x^3}{10x^4}$ is $\dfrac{20x^3}{10x^4}$. How is this simplified?

GUIDED EXAMPLES:

1. Divide. $\dfrac{72x^5 + 36x^4 + 24x^3}{12x^2}$

2. Divide. $(170x^4 - 240x^3 + 70x^2) \div (10x)$

3. Divide. $\dfrac{-42x^9 + 25x^7 + 14x^5}{-7x^4}$

4. Divide. $\dfrac{80x^8 - 32x^5 + 64x^3}{16x^4}$

Notebook 24.1
Greatest Common Factor

What are some factors of 6?
What is the factored form of 6?

When two or more numbers, variables, or algebraic expressions are multiplied, each is called a _____.

What does it mean "to factor"?

Note: What is factoring the reverse of?
How can you check your factoring?

What does it mean "to factor" a polynomial?

Factoring changes a sum/difference to a _____.

The _____ of two or more numbers is the largest number that divides exactly into each of the numbers.

Find the GCF for x^2 and x^3.

Write the procedure for finding the GCF of variable terms.

EXAMPLES 1–3 Find the GCF.
x^3, x^7, and x^5

y, y^4, and y^7

x and y^2

Now, write the procedure for finding the GCF of two or more terms with coefficients and variables.

EXAMPLE 4 Find the GCF. $9x^2$ and $15x^3$
GCF of numerical parts:
GCF of variable factors:
Product of these GCFs:

What does the Distributive Property state?

Write the steps for factoring a polynomial with common factors.

1.

2.

3.

4.

What is a prime polynomial?

EXAMPLE 5 Factor out the GCF. $9x^5 + 18x^2 + 3x$

GCF =

EXAMPLE 6 Factor out the GCF. $8x^3y + 16x^2y^2 - 24x^3y^3$

GCF =

EXAMPLES 7 & 8 Factor out the GCF.

$24ab + 12a^2 + 36a^3$

$3x + 7y + 12xy$

CONCEPT CHECK:

Why is x^3 the greatest common factor of the variable factors in
$16x^5 - 2x^4 + 4x^3$?

GUIDED EXAMPLES:.

1. Find the GCF. $4x^3$ and $10x^5$

2. Find the GCF. $4ab^3$, $8a^4b^2$, and $6a^3b^3$

3. Factor by factoring out the GCF. $4x^4 + 12x^3 + 2x$

4. Factor by factoring out the GCF. $30x^3y^2 - 24x^2y^2 + 6xy^2$

Name: _____   Date: _____

Instructor: _____   Section: _____

Notebook 24.2
Factoring by Grouping

"To factor" means to write as a _____.
A common factor of a polynomial can be a _____,
a _____, or an algebraic _____.

Write the steps for factoring by grouping.
1.

2.

3.

4.

EXAMPLE 1 Factor by grouping. $2x^2 + 3x + 6x + 9$
Group terms.
Factor within groups.
Factor entire polynomial.
Multiply to check.

Note: Sometimes you will need to factor out a _____ to
obtain two terms that contain the _____ binomial factor.

EXAMPLE 2 Factor by grouping. $2x^2 + 5x - 4x - 10$
Group terms.
Factor within groups.
Factor entire polynomial.
Multiply to check.

Caution! When factoring out a _____, check carefully!!

EXAMPLE 3 Factor by grouping. $2ax - a - 2bx + b$

EXAMPLE 4 Factor by grouping. $10x^2 - 8xy + 15x - 12y$

CONCEPT CHECK:

What is the greatest common factor for each group of terms in the polynomial $(3x^2 + 6x) + (4x + 8)$?

GUIDED EXAMPLES:.

Factor by grouping.

1. $6x^2 - 15x + 4x - 10$

2. $4x + 8y + ax + 2ay$

3. $6xy + 14x - 15y - 35$

4. $3x + 6y - 5ax - 10ay$

184

Notebook 24.6
Factoring Trinomials by Grouping Numbers (the *ac* Method)

Write the steps for factoring a polynomial by grouping.
1. Factor out a _____.
2. Group _____.
3. Factor _____ groups.
4. _____ the entire polynomial.
5. Check.

When is factor by grouping primarily used?

Factor by grouping. $2x^2 + 3x + 6x + 9$

We can also factor trinomials by this grouping method.
Write the steps for factoring trinomials by grouping.
1. Factor out a _____, if there is one.
2. Multiply __ and __.
3. Find factors of ____ that add to _____.
4. Rewrite the trinomial, and replace ___ with the
   _____ found in step 3.
5. Factor by _____.

EXAMPLE 1 Factor by the *ac*-method. $x^2 + 7x + 12$
GCF??
Multiply to find *ac*.
Find factors of *ac* that add to *b*.
Rewrite as 4 terms.
Factor by grouping.

EXAMPLE 2 Factor by the *ac*-method. $8x^2 - 19x + 6$
GCF??
Multiply to find *ac*.
Find factors of *ac* that add to *b*.
Rewrite as 4 terms.
Factor by grouping.

EXAMPLE 3 Factor by the *ac*-method. $18x^3 - 33x^2 - 21x$

GCF??

Multiply to find *ac*.

Find factors of *ac* that add to *b*.

Rewrite as 4 terms.

What happens if none of the factors of *ac* add up to *b*?

EXAMPLE 4 Factor by the *ac*-method. $3x^2 - 6x - 5$

EXAMPLE 5 Factor by the *ac*-method. $6x^2 + 11xy + 4y^2$

CONCEPT CHECK:

How should the expression $8x^2 - 10x + 3$ be rewritten with 4 terms?

GUIDED EXAMPLES: See guided examples for the specific problems.

Factor.

1. Factor. $8x^2 + 8x - 6$

2. Factor. $2x^2 + 5xz - 12z^2$

3. Factor. $18x^6 - 84x^3 + 48$

4. Factor. $4x^2 + 10x + 3$

Factoring Trinomials

Review

Multiply:

$(3x+5)(2x-1)$

To factor a trinomial of the form $ax^2 + bx + c$:

1) Write the polynomial in descending order of one variable.
2) Factor out any _____.
3) _____ the coefficients of the first and last terms (ac).
4) Find two factors of that number (ac) that add to be the coefficient of the middle term (b).
5) _____ the middle term (bx) as a sum of those factors.
6) Factor by grouping.
7) Check the factorization by multiplying.

EXAMPLE 1 Factor completely. $15n^2 - 14 - 29n$

EXAMPLE 2 Factor completely. $2y^2 + yt - 10t^2$

EXAMPLE 3 Factor completely. $x^4 - 10x^2 + 9$

EXAMPLE 4 Factor completely. $2x^2 + 26x + 64$

Helpful Hints

When factoring trinomials, there can be many factors of ac. If the trinomial can be factored, only one of these combinations adds to be the middle term. To help find this combination of factors, start with a factor of 1 and work up through the factors until you find the pair that works.

When factoring trinomials of the form $ax^2 + bx + c$, always look for the greatest common factor (GCF). This may be the only possible factoring that can be done. Do not forget to include the GCF in your final answer.

Notebook 25.1
Special Cases of Factoring

The product of a sum and a difference of binomials
$(a + b)(a - b) =$ _____, where a and b are
numbers or algebraic expressions.

EXAMPLE 1 Factor. $x^2 + 0x - 9$

How does a difference of two squares factor?

Example $x^2 - 9$

What are the 3 steps in identifying a difference of two squares?
1. The expression is a _____,
2. Both terms are _____,
3. The terms are _____.

EXAMPLES 2–4 Determine if each expression is a
difference of two squares. Tell why or why not?
$x^2 - 16$

$x^2 - 7$

$4x^2 + 81$

List the first 20 perfect square numbers:

Write the steps for factoring a difference of two squares.
1.

2.

3.

When will a sum of two squares factor?

EXAMPLES 5 & 6 Factor. Remember, $a^2 - b^2 = (a + b)(a - b)$.
$x^2 - 49$

$25b^2 - 64$

189

EXAMPLES 7 & 8 Factor.

$4x^2 - 81y^2$

$-9x^2 + 1$

A _____ is equal to $(a + b)^2 = a^2 + 2ab + b^2$,
or $(a - b)^2 = a^2 - 2ab + b^2$, where a and b are numbers or expressions.

What are the 2 steps in identifying a perfect square trinomial?
1. The first and last terms are _____,
2. The middle term is _____.

To factor a perfect square trinomial one of the formulas below.
$a^2 + 2ab + b^2 = (a + b)^2$ or $a^2 - 2ab + b^2 = (a - b)^2$.

EXAMPLES 9 & 10 Factor each of the perfect square trinomials completely.

$x^2 + 6x + 9$ $\qquad\qquad\qquad\qquad$ $9n^2 - 66n + 121$

Note: What does the middle term of the trinomial tell you about the
signs in the binomial factors?

Caution! Always look for a _____ first.

EXAMPLES 11 & 12 Factor.

$25x^2 - 100$ $\qquad\qquad\qquad\qquad$ $100x^2 + 400x + 400$

CONCEPT CHECK:
Which characteristic disqualifies $x^2 + 25$ from being a difference of squares?

GUIDED EXAMPLES:
1. Determine if the polynomial is a difference of two squares. $49r^2 - 10$

2. Factor completely. $x^2 - 121$

3. Factor completely. $x^2 + 28x + 196$

4. Factor completely. $9x^2 - 72x + 144$

Notebook 25.2
Factoring Polynomials

Factoring – A General Strategy
To factor a polynomial,
1. Look for a _____. If there is one, factor out the GCF.

2. Look at the _____ of terms.
      a. Two terms: Is it a _____?
         What is the factored form of $a^2 - b^2$?
         Math 110 only: What is the factored form of $a^3 + b^3$?
         Math 110 only: What is the factored form of $a^3 - b^3$?
      b. Three terms: Is it a _____?
         What is the factored form of $a^2 + 2ab + b^2$?
         What is the factored form of $a^2 - 2ab + b^2$?
      c. Otherwise, _____ by *ac* method.
      d. Four terms: Try to _____.

3. Always _____ by making sure all
   common factors are factored and each factor is _____.

4. Check by _____.

EXAMPLE 1 Factor completely. $3k^2 - 48$

EXAMPLE 2 Factor completely. $12n^2 - 12n - 144$

EXAMPLE 3 Factor completely. $4x^2 - 20x + 25$

EXAMPLE 4 Factor completely. $x^3 + 2x^2 - 9x - 18$

EXAMPLE 5 Factor completely. $6b^4 - 15b^2 - 36$

EXAMPLE 6 Factor completely. $12n^2 - 17n - 7$

CONCEPT CHECK:
Can $(x^2 + 4)(x^2 - 4)$ be factored further?

GUIDED EXAMPLES:
Factor completely.
1. $6x^2 - 486$

2. $10x^4 - 75x^3 + 135x^2$

3. $-2x^3 + 10x^2 + 72x - 360$

4. $6h^8 - 6$

Name: _____   Date: _____

Instructor: _____   Section: _____

Notebook 25.3
Factoring the Sum and Difference of Cubes

A difference of two squares can be factored according to the pattern of $a^2 - b^2 =$ _____, where a and b are numbers or algebraic expressions.

Can a sum of two squares factor?

Examples of differences of two squares
$x^2 - 25$

$9x^2 - 64$

$36 - x^2$

Write some examples of perfect cubes.

You will need this list of perfect cubes to identify a sum or difference of two cubes.

How do you identify a sum or difference of two cubes?

EXAMPLES 1–3 Determine if each expression is a sum of two cubes, a difference of two cubes, or neither. Tell why or why not?
$x^3 - 27$

$x^3 + 75$

$125x^6 + y^{12}$

To factor a sum of two cubes, use the formula $a^3 + b^3 = \ldots$

To factor a difference of two cube, use the formula $a^3 - b^3 = \ldots$
Caution! Pay special attention to the _____ in the factors.

Write the steps for factoring a sum or difference of two cubes.
1. Factor out any _____.

2. Write each term as a _____.

3. Write the _____ using the properties above.
Note: Will the trinomial factor ever factor?

193

EXAMPLE 4 Factor completely. $x^3 + 125$.

EXAMPLE 5 Factor completely. $x^3 - 64$

Caution! What is the first step in factoring??

EXAMPLES 6 & 7 Factor completely.
$3x^3 + 3$

$216x^3 - 64y^3$

CONCEPT CHECK:
Write the formula that can be used to factor $x^3 - 512$.

GUIDED EXAMPLES:
1. Determine if the polynomial is a sum of two cubes, a difference of two cubes, or neither. $27r^3 + 512$

2. Factor completely. $y^3 - 343$

3. Factor completely. $27x^3 + 729$

4. Factor completely. $2x^3 - 32$

Notebook 25.4
Solving Quadratic Equations by Factoring

What is the standard form of a quadratic equation?
What is the highest degree of any term in a quadratic equation?

What does the Zero Property of Multiplication state?

What is the procedure for solving a quadratic equation by factoring?
1. Make sure the equation is in _____.

2. _____, if possible.

3. Set each factor _____.

4. _____ the resulting equation.

5. _____ each solution in the original equation.

What is the most number of solutions a quadratic equation can have?
What is a double root?
When might a double root occur?

EXAMPLE 1 Solve by factoring. $x^2 + 4x = 0$
Factor.
Set each factor = 0.
Solve.
Check.

EXAMPLE 2 Solve by factoring. $2x^2 - 8x - 42 = 0$

EXAMPLE 3 Solve by factoring. $10x^2 - x = 2$
Write in standard form (set = 0)
Factor.
Set each factor = 0.
Solve.
Check.

195

EXAMPLE 4 Solve by factoring. $-5t^2 + 13t + 6 = 0$

Write in standard form (set = 0).

Factor.

Set each factor = 0.

Solve.

Check.

EXAMPLE 5 Solve by factoring. $4x^2 + 9 = 12x$

EXAMPLE 6 Solve by factoring. $x^2 - 64 = 0$

CONCEPT CHECK:

An equation has been factored to $(x + 7)(x + 6) = 0$. What are the solutions?

GUIDED EXAMPLES:

Solve by factoring.

1. $6x^2 - 12x = 0$

2. $4x^2 - 4x - 120 = 0$

3. $16x^2 = 56x - 49$

4. $-x^2 - 6x + 27 = 0$

Notebook 26.1
Undefined Rational Expressions

Any _____ can be written as a fraction of two integers.

What is a rational expression?

Give some examples of rational expressions.

Note: Do rules that work for numerical fractions work for rational expressions? Why or why not?

What does it mean if a rational expression is "undefined"?

EXAMPLE 1 Find any values of the variable that will make the rational

expression undefined. $\dfrac{15x^2 + 25x}{5x}$

Set denominator = 0.

Solve.

EXAMPLE 2 Find any value of the variable that will make the rational

expression undefined. $\dfrac{24x^2 + 9x}{8x + 3}$

Set denominator = 0.

Solve.

What does the Zero Property of Multiplication state?

EXAMPLE 3 Find any values of the variable that will make the rational

expression undefined. $\dfrac{x^3 - 9x}{x^2 + 5x + 6}$

Set denominator = 0.

Solve.

OTHER NOTES

EXAMPLE 4 Find any values of the variable that will make the rational expression undefined. $\dfrac{x^2 + 6x + 8}{x^2 - 16}$

EXAMPLE 5 Find any values of the variable that will make the rational expression undefined. $\dfrac{x^3 + 2x^2 + x + 2}{x^2 + 1}$

EXAMPLE 6 The cost to make x dozen cookies can be modeled by the expression $\dfrac{3x + 45}{4x}$. Evaluate this expression at $x = 3$ and $x = 0$. Discuss what each result means in the context of the application.
Understand the problem
Create a plan
Find the answer
Check the answer

EXAMPLE 7 The total revenue, R, in thousands of dollars, from the sale of a popular book, is given by the expression $\dfrac{1800x^2}{x^2 + 4}$, where x is the number of years since publication. Find the domain of this expression. Then find the total sales revenue of the book two years after it is published. .
Understand the problem
Create a plan
Find the answer
Check the answer

CONCEPT CHECK: Which values will make the function undefined $f(x) = \dfrac{x + 2}{x - 1}$?

GUIDED EXAMPLES: Find any values of the variable that will make the rational expression undefined.

1. $\dfrac{51x^2 + 34x}{17x}$
2. $\dfrac{72x^2 + 56x}{9x - 7}$
3. $\dfrac{8x + 72}{x^2 - 81}$

4. The yearly electrical cost to run a certain television model with a purchase price of $325 is given by the expression $\dfrac{325 + 13x}{x}$ where x is the number of years after purchase. What is the domain of this expression? What is the yearly cost to run the television four years after purchase?

198

Domain of Rational and Radical Functions

The domain is the set of all x-values that will result in a real number y-value when substituted into a function.

Rational Functions: The values that make the rational functions undefined are NOT included in the domain.

EXAMPLE 1 Specify the domain of the function. $f(x) = \dfrac{2x}{3x - 2}$

Write in set notation.
Write in interval notation.

EXAMPLE 2 Specify the domain of the function. $f(x) = \dfrac{-2}{x^2 - 5x}$

Write in set notation.
Write in interval notation.

Radical Functions: Domain and Range only deal with real numbers. The x-values in the domain will be the numbers that make the y-values be real numbers. Even roots of negative numbers are not real numbers, so the radicand must be a non-negative number.

EXAMPLE 3 Specify the domain of the function. $f(x) = \sqrt{x-2}$

Write in set notation.
Write in interval notation.

EXAMPLE 4 Specify the domain of the function. $f(x) = \sqrt{x+9}$

Write in set notation.
Write in interval notation.

Only the EVEN root of a negative number will result in non-real numbers. The odd root of any number is a real number.

EXAMPLE 5 Specify the domain of the function. $f(x) = \sqrt[3]{x}$

Write in set notation.
Write in interval notation.

200

Name: _____   Date: _____

Instructor: _____   Section: _____

Notebook 26.2
Simplifying Rational Expressions

Write the basic rule of fractions in terms of how they can be simplified.

Examples.

$$\frac{14}{21} \qquad \frac{15x}{13x} \qquad \frac{x^2+2x-3}{x^2-5x+4}$$

Caution! Only _____ can divide, not terms.
Example.

$$\frac{7+2}{1+2}$$

Which method will we use to simplify fractions?

EXAMPLE 1 Simplify. $\dfrac{21}{39}$

Factor the num. and den.
Divide by common factors.

Write the steps for simplifying rational expressions.
1.
2.
3.

EXAMPLE 2 Simplify. $\dfrac{2x+6}{3x+9}$

Factor the num. and den.
Divide by common factors.

EXAMPLE 3 Simplify. $\dfrac{x^2+9x+14}{x^2-4}$

Factor the num. and den.
Divide by common factors.

For all polynomials A and B, where $A \neq B$, $\dfrac{A-B}{B-A} = -1$.

201

EXAMPLE 4 Simplify. $\dfrac{2-x}{x-2}$

Factor the num. and den.
Divide by common factors.

EXAMPLE 5 Simplify. $\dfrac{5x^2-45}{45-15x}$

Factor the num. and den.
Divide by common factors.

EXAMPLE 6 Simplify. $\dfrac{x^2-7xy-12y^2}{2x^2-9xy+4y^2}$

Factor the num. and den.
Divide by common factors.

CONCEPT CHECK:
What is the basic rule of fractions?

GUIDED EXAMPLES:

1. Simplify by using the prime factors method. $\dfrac{105}{42}$

2. Simplify. $\dfrac{7x+42}{5x+30}$

3. Simplify. $\dfrac{3x-7}{14-6x}$

4. Simplify. $\dfrac{20-x-x^2}{3x^2-48}$

202

Notebook 26.3
Multiplying Rational Expressions

To multiply two fractions,
1. Find the _____ in the numerators and the denominators.
   Do not _____ yet.
2. _____ the numerators and denominators by
   _____.

3. Write the remaining factors as one _____.

EXAMPLE 1 Multiply. $\dfrac{12}{7} \cdot \dfrac{49}{36}$

Write the steps for multiplying rational expressions.
1. _____ the numerator and _____.
2. Find the _____. Do not multiply.
3. _____ the numerators and denominators
   by _____.
4. Write the _____ as one fraction.

What does the Quotient Rule say?

EXAMPLE 2 Multiply. $\dfrac{2x^2}{3y} \cdot \dfrac{6y}{8x}$

EXAMPLE 3 Multiply. $\dfrac{7x}{22} \cdot \dfrac{11x+33}{7x+21}$

Factor the num. and den.
Find common factors.
Divide by common factors.
Write as one fraction.

EXAMPLE 4 Multiply. $\dfrac{2x-14}{5x+25} \cdot \dfrac{x^2+7x+10}{4x-12}$

Factor the num. and den.

Find common factors.

Divide by common factors.

Write as one fraction.

Remember, $\dfrac{a-b}{b-a} = $ _____ .

EXAMPLE 5 Multiply. $\dfrac{x^2-x-12}{16-x^2} \cdot \dfrac{2x^2+7x-4}{x^2-4x-21}$

EXAMPLE 6 Multiply. $\dfrac{3x^2+7x+2}{14x+21} \cdot \dfrac{7x-14}{5x^2+6x-8}$

CONCEPT CHECK:

What are the common factors when multiplying $\dfrac{2x^2}{y} \cdot \dfrac{6}{x}$?

GUIDED EXAMPLES:

1. Multiply. $\dfrac{-45x^3}{26y} \cdot \dfrac{39y}{30x^2}$

2. Multiply. $\dfrac{8x}{9} \cdot \dfrac{6x-36}{8x-48}$

3. Multiply. $\dfrac{x^2-5x-6}{x^2-2x-3} \cdot \dfrac{4x^2+17x-42}{x^2-36}$

4. Multiply. $\dfrac{x^4-1}{3x^2+3} \cdot \dfrac{12x^2+6x}{5x^3+8x^2+3x}$

204

Notebook 26.4
Dividing Rational Expressions

To divide two fractions,
1. Find the _____ of the second fraction
   and _____ the first fraction by this _____.
2. Find the _____ in the numerators
   and denominators. Do not multiply yet. _____.
3. _____ by common _____.
4. Write the remaining factors as one _____.

EXAMPLE 1 Divide. $\dfrac{12}{7} \div \dfrac{36}{49}$

Write the steps for dividing rational expressions.
1. Find the _____ of the second expression and
   _____ the first expression by this _____.

2. Factor the _____. Do not multiply.
3. _____ the numerators and denominators
   by _____.
4. Write the _____ as one fraction.

EXAMPLE 2 Divide. $\dfrac{-12x^2}{5y} \div \dfrac{18x}{15y}$

Multiply by the reciprocal.

EXAMPLE 3 Divide. $\dfrac{8x}{14} \div \dfrac{8x-32}{7x-28}$

Multiply by the reciprocal.

EXAMPLE 4 Divide. $\dfrac{x^2+3x-10}{x^2+x-20} \div \dfrac{x^2+4x+3}{x^2-3x-4}$

Remember, $\dfrac{a-b}{b-a} = $ _____

EXAMPLE 5 Divide. $\dfrac{x-5}{3} \div (25-x^2)$

CONCEPT CHECK:

Rewrite $\dfrac{x-2}{4} \div (x^2-4)$ as a multiplication problem.

GUIDED EXAMPLES:

1. Divide. $\dfrac{9x^3}{35y^2} \div \dfrac{27x}{7y}$

2. Divide. $\dfrac{16x^2-6x-7}{24x^2-29x+7} \div \dfrac{10x^2+x-2}{15x^2+x-2}$

3. Divide. $\dfrac{6x-7}{4} \div (49-36x^2)$

4. Divide. $\dfrac{3x+2}{x+4} \cdot \dfrac{x^2-16}{4x+3}$

206

Notebook 27.1
Adding Like Rational Expressions

A _____ can be written as a fraction of two algebraic expressions.

What are like rational expressions?

Write some examples of like rational expressions.

What is the rule for adding like rational expressions?

Write the steps for adding like rational expressions.
1.

2.

EXAMPLE 1 Add. $\dfrac{5a}{4a+2b}+\dfrac{6a}{4a+2b}$

Add the numerators.
Keep the denominator.
Simplify.

Why do you not divide the a from the answer?

EXAMPLE 2 Add. $\dfrac{-7m}{2n}+\dfrac{m}{2n}$

Add the numerators.
Keep the denominator.
Simplify.

Note: Simplify whenever possible by _____,
_____, and _____ common factors.

EXAMPLE 3 Add. $\dfrac{-3}{x^2-3x+2}+\dfrac{x+1}{x^2-3x+2}$

EXAMPLES 4 & 5 Add.

$$\frac{x+3}{x^2-1}+\frac{x}{x^2-1}$$

$$\frac{x}{x+1}+\frac{1}{x+1}$$

CONCEPT CHECK:

Is $\dfrac{2x+2}{x+1}$ written in simplest form?

GUIDED EXAMPLES:

1. Add. $\dfrac{-4b}{5a+b}+\dfrac{b}{5a+b}$

2. Add. $\dfrac{p}{12q}+\dfrac{2p}{12q}$

3. Add. $\dfrac{2x^2-8x}{2x-5}+\dfrac{x+5}{2x-5}$

4. Add. $\dfrac{2x}{x^2+5x+6}+\dfrac{x+2}{x^2+5x+6}$

208

Notebook 27.2
Subtracting Like Rational Expressions

A rational expression can be written as a fraction of two
_____.

Rational expressions with a common denominator are called
_____.

To add like rational expressions.
1. _____ the numerators and _____ the denominator.
2. _____ if possible.

What does "Leave, Change, Change" mean?

What is the rule for subtracting like rational expressions?

Write the steps for subtracting like rational expressions.
1.

2.

EXAMPLE 1 Subtract. $\dfrac{-2a}{3b} - \dfrac{5a}{3b}$

Subtract the numerators.
Keep the denominator.
Simplify.

EXAMPLE 2 Subtract. $\dfrac{8x}{2x+3y} - \dfrac{3x}{2x+3y}$

Subtract the numerators.
Keep the denominator.
Simplify.

Why is the x not divided out of the answer?

Note: Be sure to treat the numerator of the fraction
being subtracted as a single quantity. How do you do this?

EXAMPLE 3 Subtract. $\dfrac{3x^2+2x}{x^2-1}-\dfrac{10x-5}{x^2-1}$

EXAMPLES 4 & 5 Subtract.

$\dfrac{3x}{x-4}-\dfrac{12}{x-4}$

$\dfrac{3x}{x^2+3x+2}-\dfrac{2x-8}{x^2+3x+2}$

CONCEPT CHECK:

Is $\dfrac{2c-4}{8c}$ written in simplest form?

GUIDED EXAMPLES:

1. Subtract. $\dfrac{5x}{2x-10}-\dfrac{6}{2x-10}$

2. Subtract. $\dfrac{10m}{2m+n}-\dfrac{7m+4}{2m+n}$

3. Subtract. $\dfrac{-8a}{3b}-\dfrac{a}{3b}$

4. Subtract. $\dfrac{2y}{2y-7}-\dfrac{7}{2y-7}$

210

Notebook 27.3
Finding the Least Common Denominator for Rational Expressions

To add and subtract rational expressions when the denominators are not the same, first find the _____.

What is the LCD?

Write the steps for finding the LCD of two or more expressions.
1. _____ each denominator.
2. List each _____.
3. For each factor, put the _____ that appears on each factor.
4. The LCD is the _____ of these _____.

Note: If a factor occurs more than once in any one denominator, how many times does the LCD contain that factor?

EXAMPLE 1 Find the LCD. $\dfrac{5}{2x-4}, \dfrac{6}{3x-6}$

Factor each denominator.
List each different factor.
Put the highest exponent on each factor.
LCD =

EXAMPLE 2 Find the LCD. $\dfrac{5}{12ab^2c}, \dfrac{13}{18a^3bc^4}$

Factor each denominator.
List each different factor.
Line up the factors.
Put the highest exponent on each factor.
LCD =

Caution! Be careful when comparing common _____.

EXAMPLES 3–5 Find the LCD.

$$\frac{5}{x+3}, \frac{2}{x-4}$$

$$\frac{8}{x^2-5x+4}, \frac{12}{x^2+2x-3}$$

$$\frac{x+3}{x^2-6x+9}, \frac{10}{2x^2-4x-6}, \frac{x}{2}$$

CONCEPT CHECK:

How many times will $(x-1)$ be included in the LCD

for $\dfrac{x}{(x-1)^2}, \dfrac{1}{x-1}$?

GUIDED EXAMPLES:

1. Find the LCD. $\dfrac{7}{6x+21}, \dfrac{13}{10x+35}$

2. Find the LCD. $\dfrac{3}{50xy^2z}, \dfrac{19}{40x^3yz}$

3. Find the LCD. $\dfrac{2}{x^2+5x+6}, \dfrac{6}{3x^2+5x-2}$

4. Find the LCD. $\dfrac{x-3}{x^3+8x^2+16x}, \dfrac{7x}{6x^2+18x-24}, \dfrac{5}{x}$

Notebook 27.4
Adding and Subtracting Unlike Rational Expressions

To add or subtract _____ fractions, first rewrite each fraction using the
_____. Then _____ or _____, and simplify, if possible.

Write the steps for writing equivalent rational expressions with a least common
denominator.
1. Find the _____.

2. For each rational expression, find the _____ that you
   need to _____ the denominator by to get the _____.

3. Rewrite each rational expression as an _____
   rational expression whose _____ is the LCD.
   For each rational expression, multiply the _____
   and _____ by the expression found in step 2.

EXAMPLE 1 Write equivalent rational expressions using the LCD.

$\dfrac{8}{ab}, \dfrac{5}{a^2}$ LCD =

Write the steps for adding and subtracting rational expressions.
1. If the rational expressions have _____ denominators,
   find the _____. Otherwise, go straight to step 3.

2. _____ each rational expression with the LCD
   as the _____.

3. Add or subtract the _____, and keep the _____.

4. _____ if possible.

EXAMPLE 2 Add. $\dfrac{5}{xy} + \dfrac{2}{y}$

LCD =
Rewrite as equivalent fractions.
Add numerators.
Keep denominator.

EXAMPLE 3 Add. $\dfrac{3x}{x^2 - y^2} + \dfrac{5}{x + y}$

LCD =
Equivalent fractions.
Add numerators.
Keep denominator.
Simplify.

EXAMPLE 4 Add. $\dfrac{4y}{y^2 + 4y + 3} + \dfrac{2}{y + 1}$

Caution! Why is it helpful to place parentheses around the numerator of the second fraction when subtracting?

EXAMPLE 5 Subtract. $\dfrac{3x - 4}{x - 2} - \dfrac{5x - 6}{2x - 4}$

EXAMPLE 6 Subtract. $\dfrac{-3}{x^2 + 8x + 15} - \dfrac{1}{2x^2 + 7x + 3}$

CONCEPT CHECK:

What is the LCD for the following sum, $\dfrac{3}{x} + \dfrac{2}{x - 1}$?

GUIDED EXAMPLES:

1. Add. $\dfrac{7}{a} + \dfrac{3}{ab}$

2. Add. $\dfrac{7x}{x^2 + 2xy + y^2} + \dfrac{4}{x^2 + xy}$

3. Subtract. $\dfrac{x + 7}{3x - 9} - \dfrac{x - 6}{x - 3}$

4. Subtract. $\dfrac{x}{x^2 + 2x - 3} - \dfrac{x}{x^2 - 5x + 4}$

214

Notebook 28.1
Simplifying Complex Rational Expressions by Adding and Subtracting

What is a complex rational expression?

Write some examples of complex rational expressions.

Note: What does the fraction bar in a complex fraction mean?

To add or subtract fractions, you must have a _____.

For which type of complex fraction problem does this method of simplifying a complex rational expression work best for?

Write the steps for simplifying a complex rational expressions by inverting and multiplying.
1. If necessary, simplify the _____ into a single fraction.
2. If necessary, simplify the _____ into a single fraction.
3. _____ the fraction in the _____ by the _____
    in the _____. To do this, _____ the fraction in the
    _____ and _____ it by the _____.
4. _____, if possible.

EXAMPLE 1 Simplify. $\dfrac{\frac{1}{x}}{\frac{2}{y^2}+\frac{1}{y}}$

True/False A complex rational expression may contain two or more fractions in the numerator and the denominator.

EXAMPLE 2 Simplify. $\dfrac{\frac{1}{x}+\frac{1}{y}}{\frac{3}{x}-\frac{2}{y}}$

Numerator as a single fraction.
Denominator as a single fraction.
Invert and multiply.

EXAMPLE 3 Simplify. $\dfrac{\frac{1}{x^2-1}+\frac{2}{x+1}}{x}$

Numerator as a single fraction.

Denominator as a single fraction.

Invert and multiply

EXAMPLE 4 Simplify. $\dfrac{\frac{3}{a+b}-\frac{3}{a-b}}{\frac{5}{a^2-b^2}}$

CONCEPT CHECK:

Write an example of a complex fraction with two fractions
in the numerator and two in the denominator?

GUIDED EXAMPLES:

1. Simplify. $\dfrac{\frac{1}{a}+\frac{1}{a^2}}{\frac{2}{b^2}}$

2. Simplify. $\dfrac{\frac{1}{x}+\frac{1}{y}}{\frac{x}{2}-\frac{5}{y}}$

3. Simplify. $\dfrac{\frac{x}{x^2+4x+3}+\frac{2}{x+1}}{x+1}$

4. Simplify. $\dfrac{\frac{6}{x^2-y^2}}{\frac{1}{x-y}+\frac{3}{x+y}}$

Notebook 28.3
Solving Rational Equations

The _____ states that if both sides of an equation are multiplied by the same non-zero number, the solution does not change.

Write the steps for solving an equation containing rational expressions.
1. Find the _____ of all the denominators.
2. _____ each term of the equation by the _____.
3. _____, then solve the resulting equation.
4. Check. Any value that would make a _____ equal to _____ must be _____ from the solution.

EXAMPLE 1 Solve for x. $\dfrac{5}{x}+\dfrac{2}{3}=-\dfrac{3}{x}$.

LCD =
Multiply each term by the LCD.
Solve.

EXAMPLE 2 Solve for x. $\dfrac{6}{x+3}=\dfrac{3}{x}$

LCD =

EXAMPLE 3 Solve for x. $\dfrac{3}{x+5}-1=\dfrac{4-x}{2x+10}$.

LCD =

What is an extraneous solution?

Why is it important that you check all apparent solutions in the original equation?

How many solutions will there be?

EXAMPLE 4 Solve for x. $\dfrac{y}{y-2} - 4 = \dfrac{2}{y-2}$

LCD =

Make sure you check your solution. What happens?

CONCEPT CHECK:

What is the first step in solving a rational equation?

GUIDED EXAMPLES:

1. Solve for x. $\dfrac{6}{3x-5} = \dfrac{3}{2x}$

2. Solve for x. $\dfrac{3}{x+3} + \dfrac{9}{x^2+3x} = \dfrac{x-2}{x}$

3. Solve for x. $\dfrac{2x}{x+1} = \dfrac{-2}{x+1} + 1$

4. Solve for x. $\dfrac{x+11}{x^2-5x+4} + \dfrac{3}{x-1} = \dfrac{5}{x-4}$

Notebook 30.1
Square Roots

The _____ is one of two identical factors of a number.
What does it mean to "take the square root" of a number?

What symbol is used to denote the positive square root of a number?

How do we denote the negative square root?

EXAMPLES 1–4 Find the square roots.

$\sqrt{100}$

$\sqrt{\dfrac{9}{25}}$

$-\sqrt{49}$

$\sqrt{0}$

EXAMPLES 5 & 6 Simplify.

$\sqrt{5^2}$

$\sqrt{(-5)^2}$

For any real number a, $\sqrt{a^2}$ = _____.

We are going to assume that if a variable appears in the radicand, then
it represents a …

EXAMPLES 7 & 8 Find the square roots.

$\sqrt{49x^2}$

$\sqrt{(-6x)^2}$

What happens when you try to simplify $\sqrt{-25}$?

What can you say about the square root of any negative number?

What about a negative square root of a negative number, like $-\sqrt{-36}$?
Explain.

219

EXAMPLES 9 & 10 Find the square roots.

$\sqrt{-144}$

$-\sqrt{-9}$

EXAMPLE 11 Use a calculator to approximate $\sqrt{3}$.
Round to the nearest hundredth.

Explain how you can approximate a square root if you do not have a calculator.

EXAMPLE 12 Approximate $\sqrt{75}$ by finding two consecutive whole numbers that the square root lies between.

CONCEPT CHECK:
What is the principal square root of 9?

GUIDED EXAMPLES:

1. Find the square root. If the square root is not a real number, say so. $\sqrt{121}$

2. Find the square root. If the square root is not a real number, say so.
   $-\sqrt{-81}$

3. Find the square root. If the square root is not a real number, say so.
   Assume all variables represent nonnegative numbers. $-\sqrt{121a^2}$

4. Use a calculator to approximate the square root to the nearest hundredth.
   $-\sqrt{84}$

220

Notebook 30.2
Higher Order Roots

The _____ is one of two identical factors of a number.
What does it mean to "take the square root" of a number?

How is a higher-order root written?
What is the n called?
What is the a called?
Note: What is the index of a square root?

What is the cube root of a number?
What is the index of a cube root?

Example $\sqrt[3]{8}$

Let's look at higher powers...
Complete the table. Keep it handy, you will use it often.

x	x^2	x^3	x^4	x^5
1				
2				
3				
4				
5				
6				
7				
8				
9				
10				

EXAMPLES 1 – 3 Find the cube roots.
$\sqrt[3]{27x^3}$

$-\sqrt[3]{\dfrac{8}{27}}$

$\sqrt[3]{-1}$

Why is it ok to have a cube root of a negative number?
The cube root of a negative number is a _____.

What is meant by the nth root?

221

EXAMPLES 4 & 5 Find the indicated roots.

$\sqrt[5]{32}$

$\sqrt[4]{-81}$

When must the radicand be nonnegative?
It is impossible to take an _____ root of a _____ number!

EXAMPLES 6–8 Simplify the radicals.

$\sqrt[5]{x^{10}}$

How can you find an nth root when the radicand contains variables?

$\sqrt[4]{y^{12}}$

$\sqrt[4]{a^{24}b^{28}}$

EXAMPLES 9 & 10 Simplify the radicals.

$\sqrt[3]{-64x^6}$

$\sqrt[4]{10,000x^4}$

CONCEPT CHECK:
Write a radical expression that has an index of 4.

GUIDED EXAMPLES:

1. Find the cube root. $\sqrt[3]{-64}$

2. Find the cube root. $-\sqrt[3]{\dfrac{a^6}{125}}$

3. Find the indicated root. $\sqrt[5]{x^{30}}$

4. Find the indicated root. $\sqrt[5]{-32x^5}$

222

Notebook 30.3
Simplifying Radical Expressions

OTHER NOTES

The _____ is one of two identical factors of a number.
Examples.

What does the Product Rule for Radicals state?

Again, what assumption will be made about variables inside radicals?

EXAMPLE 1 Simplify the radical. $\sqrt{50}$

EXAMPLES 2 & 3 Find the indicated roots.
$\sqrt{8}$

$\sqrt{48}$

EXAMPLE 4 Simplify, if possible. $\sqrt[3]{-54}$

How do you find an nth root?
Example.

EXAMPLES 5 & 6 Simplify the radicals. Assume all variables represent nonnegative values.
$\sqrt{x^5}$

$\sqrt[3]{y^{17}}$

EXAMPLES 7 & 8 Simplify the radicals. Assume all variables represent nonnegative values.
$\sqrt{24x^3}$

$\sqrt[3]{-16x^{11}}$

How can you simplify radicals if you do not know perfect root factors?

EXAMPLE 9 Simplify. Assume all variables represent nonnegative values.

$\sqrt[3]{500x^5y^7}$

CONCEPT CHECK:

What is the remainder when $\sqrt[6]{x^{17}}$ is simplified?
(That is, what remains under the radical?)

GUIDED EXAMPLES:

1. Simplify. Assume all variables represent nonnegative values. $\sqrt{1000a^3}$

2. Simplify. $\sqrt[3]{250y^3}$

3. Simplify. $\sqrt[3]{\dfrac{81}{8}}$

4. Simplify. $\sqrt[3]{128x^5y^4}$

Notebook 30.4
Rational Exponents

How do you write rational exponents as radicals?

If n is an integer greater than 1, with $\dfrac{1}{n}$ in simplest form,

then…

The denominator of the rational exponent becomes the _____.

EXAMPLES 1 & 2 Write in radical notation. Simplify, if possible.

$9^{\frac{1}{2}}$

$x^{\frac{1}{3}}$

Note: What does a $\dfrac{1}{2}$ power mean?

What does a $\dfrac{1}{3}$ power mean?

What is the rule for writing rational exponents as radicals?

If m and n are integers greater than 1, with $\dfrac{m}{n}$ in simplest form,

then…

EXAMPLES 3 & 4 Write in radical notation. Simplify, if possible.

$6^{\frac{2}{3}}$

$x^{\frac{3}{2}}$

EXAMPLES 5 & 6 Use radical notation to rewrite each expression.
Simplify, if possible.

$\left(\dfrac{1}{9}\right)^{\frac{3}{2}}$

$(3x)^{\frac{1}{3}}$

What does a negative exponent mean?
How do you simplify an exponential expression that has a negative
rational exponent?

EXAMPLES 7 & 8 Evaluate the expressions.

$25^{-\frac{3}{2}}$

$-16^{-\frac{3}{4}}$

Write the product rule for exponents.

Write the quotient rule for exponents.

EXAMPLES 9 & 10 Use the rules of exponents to simplify.

$\dfrac{6^{\frac{1}{3}}}{6^{\frac{4}{3}}}$

$x^{\frac{1}{2}} \cdot x^{\frac{1}{3}}$

CONCEPT CHECK:

What would be the fastest way to simplify $\dfrac{7^{\frac{5}{6}}}{7^{\frac{2}{3}}}$?

GUIDED EXAMPLES:

1. Write in radical form. Simplify if possible. Assume all variables represent nonnegative values. $-x^{\frac{3}{5}}$

2. Simplify. $9^{\frac{5}{2}}$

3. Simplify. Write your answer in radical notation. Assume all variables represent nonnegative values. $x^{\frac{2}{5}} \cdot x^{\frac{1}{2}}$

4. Simplify. $\dfrac{7^{\frac{1}{5}}}{7^{\frac{6}{5}}}$

Notebook 31.2
Adding and Subtracting Radical Expressions

_____ are terms that have the same variables raised to the same powers.

EXAMPLES 1–3 Combine like terms.

$7x + 9x$

$13xy^2 + 11x^2y$

$5x^{1/2} + 2x^{1/2}$

What does the rational rule for exponents say?

If m and n are real numbers greater than 1 with $\dfrac{m}{n}$ in simplest form, then…

A _____ is written using the radical sign, _____, where n is the _____ and a is the _____.

What are like radicals?

Give some examples of like radicals.

Give some examples of unlike radicals. Tell why they are unlike.

Write the steps for adding and subtracting radical expressions.
1.
2.
Note: Only _____ can be added or subtracted.

EXAMPLES 4–6 Simplify, if possible. Assume that all variables are nonnegative real numbers.

$5\sqrt{3} + 7\sqrt{3}$

$3\sqrt{2} - 9\sqrt{2}$

$-6\sqrt{xy} + 2\sqrt[3]{xy}$

The Product Rules for radicals says that for all nonnegative real
real numbers a, b, and n, where n is an integer greater than 1, …

EXAMPLE 7 Simplify. $\sqrt{50} + \sqrt{18}$

Simplify each radical term.

Combine like radicals.

EXAMPLE 8 Simplify. $5\sqrt{3} - \sqrt{27} + 2\sqrt{32}$
Simplify each radical term.

Combine like radicals.

EXAMPLE 9 Simplify. Assume that all variables are nonnegative real numbers. $6\sqrt{x} + 4\sqrt{12x} - \sqrt{75x} + 3\sqrt{x}$

EXAMPLE 10 Simplify. Assume that all variables are nonnegative real numbers. $3x\sqrt[3]{54x^4} - 3\sqrt[3]{16x^7}$

CONCEPT CHECK:
Can $\sqrt{50}$ and $3\sqrt{5}$ be combined?

GUIDED EXAMPLES:
1. Simplify. If the radicals cannot be combined, state why. Assume variables represent nonnegative numbers.
   $4\sqrt{11} - 7\sqrt{11}$

2. Simplify. $\sqrt{54} + \sqrt{24}$

3. Simplify. Assume variables represent nonnegative numbers.
   $\sqrt{18x} - x\sqrt{80x} + 7\sqrt{2x} - \sqrt{5x^3}$

4. Simplify. $\sqrt[3]{24n^7} - 4n\sqrt[3]{81n^4}$

228

Notebook 31.3
Multiplying Radical Expressions

The Distributive Property says that for a, b, and c, $a(b + c) =$ _____ .

EXAMPLE 1 Multiply.

$$-6\left(\sqrt{2} + \sqrt{3}\right)$$

The Product Rule for Radicals states that for all nonnegative real numbers a, b, and n, where n is an integer greater than 1, …

EXAMPLE 2 Multiply.

$$\sqrt{5} \cdot \sqrt{3}$$

To multiply monomials, first multiply the _____ , and then _____ the variables.

Multiply. $4x \cdot 3y$

EXAMPLE 3 Multiply. Assume all variables represent nonnegative numbers.

$-7x \cdot 9xy$ $-7\sqrt{x} \cdot 9\sqrt{2x}$

EXAMPLE 4 Multiply. $\left(\sqrt{12}\right)\left(-5\sqrt{3}\right)$

EXAMPLE 5 Multiply. $\left(\sqrt[3]{2x}\right)\left(\sqrt[3]{4x^2} + 3\sqrt[3]{y}\right)$

To multiply binomials,
1.
2.

Multiply $(a + b)(c + d)$ using the FOIL method.

EXAMPLE 6 Multiply. $\left(\sqrt{2}+3\sqrt{5}\right)\left(2\sqrt{2}-\sqrt{5}\right)$

Note: Remember, $\left(\sqrt{x}\right)^2 =$

Examples.

$\left(\sqrt{3}\right)^2$ $\qquad\qquad$ $\left(\sqrt{7y}\right)^2$

If a and b are numbers or expressions, $(a+b)(a-b) =$

EXAMPLE 7 Multiply. $\left(5+3\sqrt{2}\right)\left(5-3\sqrt{2}\right)$

If a and b are numbers or expressions, $(a+b)^2 =$
and $(a-b)^2 =$

EXAMPLE 8 Simplify. Assume all variables represent nonnegative numbers.

$\left(\sqrt{7}+\sqrt{3x}\right)^2$

CONCEPT CHECK:

How many radicals will be left in the final answer when $\left(\sqrt{2}-3\sqrt{6}\right)\left(\sqrt{2}-\sqrt{6}\right)$ is multiplied?

GUIDED EXAMPLES:

1. Multiply. $\left(3\sqrt{28}\right)\left(4\sqrt{2}\right)$

2. Multiply. Assume all variables represent nonnegative numbers.
$\sqrt{6x}\left(2\sqrt{3x}+5\sqrt{2}\right)$

3. Multiply. $\left(6+2\sqrt{5}\right)\left(8-\sqrt{7}\right)$

4. Simplify. Assume all variables represent nonnegative numbers.
$\left(\sqrt{3x}-2\sqrt{5}\right)^2$

Name: _____   Date: _____

Instructor: _____   Section: _____

Notebook 31.4
Dividing Radical Expressions

For all nonnegative real numbers a, b, and n, where n is an integer greater than
1, $\sqrt[n]{a} \cdot \sqrt[n]{b} =$ _____   (The Product Rule for Radicals)

The Quotient Rule for Radicals states that for all nonnegative real numbers
a, b, and n, where n is an integer greater than 1 and $b \neq 0$, $\dfrac{\sqrt[n]{a}}{\sqrt[n]{b}} =$

EXAMPLE 1 Divide. $\dfrac{\sqrt{75}}{\sqrt{3}}$

Write the procedure for dividing radical expressions.
If you can easily take the _____ of both the _____
and _____, take the _____ first, then _____.
If you can easily _____ first, _____, and then
take the _____.

EXAMPLES 2 & 3 Divide.

$\dfrac{\sqrt{9}}{\sqrt{16}}$

$\dfrac{\sqrt{72}}{\sqrt{8}}$

EXAMPLES 4 & 5 Divide. Assume all variables represent nonnegative
values.

$\sqrt[3]{\dfrac{-a^9}{b^6}}$

$\dfrac{\sqrt[3]{x^8}}{\sqrt[3]{x^5}}$

EXAMPLE 6 Divide. Assume all variables represent nonnegative values.

$$\frac{\sqrt{54a^3b^7}}{\sqrt{6b^5}}$$

EXAMPLE 7 Divide. Assume all variables represent nonnegative values.

$$\frac{\sqrt{25x^5y^2}}{\sqrt{144x^3y^4}}$$

CONCEPT CHECK:

For $\dfrac{\sqrt{72}}{\sqrt{8}}$ would it be easier to take the root of the fraction or divide first and then take the root?

GUIDED EXAMPLES:

1. Divide. Assume all variables represent nonnegative numbers.

$$\frac{\sqrt{98}}{\sqrt{2}}$$

2. Divide. $\dfrac{\sqrt{144}}{\sqrt{4}}$

3. Divide. Assume variables represent positive values.

$$\frac{\sqrt{48a^9b^5}}{\sqrt{3a^7b}}$$

4. Divide. Assume variables represent positive values.

$$\sqrt{\frac{80a^5b^3}{5a^3b^9}}$$

232

Notebook 31.5
Rationalizing the Denominator

A _____ can be written as a fraction of two integers.
A rational number written in decimal form will either _____
or _____.
Write some examples of rational numbers.

What are irrational numbers?
Give some examples.

What does the Identity Property of Multiplication say?

Rationalizing the Denominator means…
removing a _____ from a denominator.
This means changing the _____ from a _____
number to a _____ number.

How do you "rationalize a denominator"?

EXAMPLE 1 Simplify by rationalizing the denominator. $\dfrac{1}{\sqrt{2}}$

EXAMPLE 2 Simplify by rationalizing the denominator. $\dfrac{3x}{\sqrt{12x^2}}$

EXAMPLE 3 Simplify by rationalizing the denominator. $\sqrt[3]{\dfrac{2}{3x^2}}$

Remember, $(a + b)(a - b) =$

What are conjugates?

Give some examples of conjugates. What are their products?

Note. What can you say about the product of two conjugates?

EXAMPLE 4 Simplify by rationalizing the denominator. $\dfrac{5}{3+\sqrt{2}}$

EXAMPLE 5 Simplify by rationalizing the denominator. $\dfrac{\sqrt{7}+\sqrt{3}}{\sqrt{7}-\sqrt{3}}$

CONCEPT CHECK:

What should $\dfrac{2}{3+\sqrt{5}}$ be multiplied by in order to rationalize the denominator?

GUIDED EXAMPLES:

1. Simplify by rationalizing the denominator. Assume that all variables represent nonnegative numbers and $y \neq 0$.

   $\dfrac{\sqrt{7x}}{\sqrt{14y}}$

2. Simplify by rationalizing the denominator. $\sqrt[3]{\dfrac{3}{5x^2}}$

3. Simplify by rationalizing the denominator. $\dfrac{4}{2+\sqrt{5}}$

4. Simplify by rationalizing the denominator. $\dfrac{\sqrt{3}+\sqrt{10}}{\sqrt{3}-\sqrt{10}}$

234

Name: _____   Date: _____

Instructor: _____   Section: _____

Notebook 31.6
Solving Radical Equations

What are examples of reverse operations?

What is the Squaring Property of Equality?

Examples.

Write the steps for solving equations containing radicals.
1.

2.
　　　*

　　　*

3.

4.

5.

EXAMPLE 1 Solve. $\sqrt{x} = 7$.
Square both sides.

EXAMPLE 2 Solve. $\sqrt{x} = -8$.
Square both sides.

Check.

EXAMPLE 3 Solve. $3 + \sqrt{x-5} = 15$.
Get the radical by itself.

Square both sides.

Solve.

Check.

EXAMPLE 4 Solve. $\sqrt{5x+6} = x$.

Square both sides.

Solve.

Check.

Why is −1 not a solution?

EXAMPLE 5 Solve. $-6 + \sqrt[3]{x} = -10$.

Get the radical by itself.

Cube both sides.

Solve.

Check.

EXAMPLE 6 The Body Mass Index, BMI, is an indirect measure of a person's body fat based on height and weight. One formula involving BMI is

$h = \sqrt{\dfrac{w}{\text{BMI}}}$, where w is the person's weight in kilograms and h is the height in

meters. Solve this equation for BMI, and then use this result to determine if the BMI for a person who is 1.8 meters tall and weighs 66 kilograms is healthy. Note: The healthy BMI range is between 18.5 and 24.9.

CONCEPT CHECK:
True/False Raising a number to a power and taking a root of a power are reverse operations.

GUIDED EXAMPLES:

1. Solve. $\sqrt{x} = 13$

2. Solve. $-6 + \sqrt{x} = 3$

3. Solve. $\sqrt{x+2} = x$

4. Solve. $\sqrt{(x+1)} + 3 = 7$

236

Name: _____   Date: _____

Instructor: _____   Section: _____

Notebook 32.1
Introduction to Solving Quadratic Equations

What is the standard form of a quadratic equation?
What is the highest degree of any term in a quadratic equation?

EXAMPLES 1–3 Write each quadratic equation in standard form.

$7x^2 = 5x + 8$

$6x - 2x^2 = -3$

$4x^2 = 9$

What is the graph of a quadratic equation called?
What do they look like? (Sketch both cases.)

What is the y-coordinate of the x-intercept?
What is the x-coordinate of the x-intercept?

The _____ of an equation is the number(s) that, when substituted for the variable(s), make(s) the equation true.

The _____ is the graph of an equation is/are the _____ where the curve crosses the _____.

Note: How many x-intercepts will the graph of a quadratic equation have?

The _____ to the quadratic equation are the _____ of the x-intercepts.

EXAMPLES 4–6 Determine the number of solutions for each quadratic graphed below.

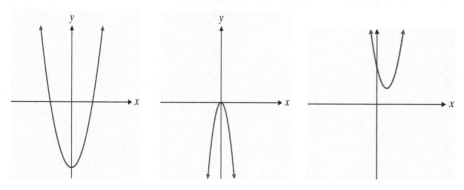

EXAMPLES 7 & 8 Find the real solution(s) of each quadratic equation, if any exist, by using the graph of the equation.

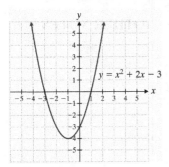

$y = x^2 + 2x - 3$

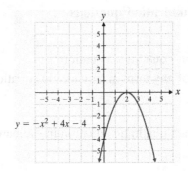

$y = -x^2 + 4x - 4$

CONCEPT CHECK:

If a quadratic equation has two solutions, how many x-intercepts does it have?

GUIDED EXAMPLES: See guided examples.

1. Write each equation in standard form. $8x + 1 = 5x^2$

2. Determine how many solutions the quadratic equation represented by each graph has.

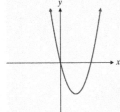

3. Find the real solution(s) of the quadratic equation, if any exist, by using the graph of the equation.

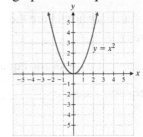

$y = x^2$

4. Find the real solution(s) of the quadratic equation, if any exist, by using the graph of the equation..

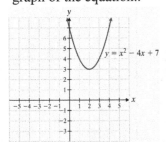

$y = x^2 - 4x + 7$

238

Notebook 32.2
Solving Quadratic Equations by Factoring

Write the steps for solving a quadratic equation by factoring.
1. Make sure the equation is in _____.
2. _____, if possible.
3. Set each factor _____.
4. _____ the resulting equations.
5. _____ each solution in the original equation.

Note. What happens if the quadratic expression does not factor?

EXAMPLE 1 Solve by factoring. $x^2 - 9x = 0$
Factor.
Set each factor = 0.
Solve.
Check.

EXAMPLE 2 Solve by factoring. $5x^2 - 14x - 3 = 0$
Factor.
Set each factor = 0.
Solve.
Check.

EXAMPLE 3 Solve by factoring. $9x^2 = 24x - 15$
Write in standard form (set = 0).
Factor.
Set each factor = 0.
Solve.
Check.

EXAMPLE 4 Solve by factoring. $x^2 - 2x = -1$

Write in standard form (set = 0).

Factor.

Set each factor = 0.

Solve.

Check.

CONCEPT CHECK:

What is the first step to solve $x^2 = 3x$ by factoring?

GUIDED EXAMPLES:

Solve by factoring.

1. $2x^2 + 16x = 0$

2. $3x^2 + 8x - 35 = 0$

3. $5x^2 + 60 = 35x$

4. $x^2 + 6x + 9 = 0$

240

Notebook 32.3
Solving Quadratic Equations Using the Square Root Property

A _____ is an equation that can be written in the
form _____ where $a \neq 0$.
This is called _____ form of a quadratic equation.
What is the highest degree of any term in a quadratic equation?

What does the Square Root Property (SRP) say?

Note: What is the shorthand way of writing $+\sqrt{a}$ or $-\sqrt{a}$?

EXAMPLE 1 Solve for x. $x^2 = 36$
Use the SRP.
Simplify.
Check.

Caution! Don't forget to use the _____. Otherwise, you will get
_____ of the two solutions.

EXAMPLE 2 Solve for x. $x^2 = 48$
Use the SRP.
Simplify.
Check.

Caution! The Square Root Property can only be used to solve one type
of equation. What form must it be in?

EXAMPLE 3 Solve for x. $x^2 = -4$
Use the SRP.
Simplify.
Check.

Note: What can you say about an equation of the form $x^2 = a$ negative number?

Note: Sometimes you will need to perform steps to get the _____ alone on one side of the equation.

EXAMPLE 4 Solve for x. $3x^2 + 2 = 77$

Note: Can the Square Root Property be used to solve quadratic equations in which the base is an algebraic expression?

EXAMPLE 5 Solve for x. $(4x - 1)^2 = 5$

CONCEPT CHECK:
True/False The Square Root Property can only be used for equations in the form of $x^2 = a$ if a is a perfect square.

GUIDED EXAMPLES:

1. Solve for x.
   $x^2 = 49$

2. Solve for x.
   $x^2 = 18$

3. Solve for x.
   $x^2 = -25$

4. Solve for x.
   $(2x + 3)^2 = 7$

Notebook 32.4
Solving Quadratic Equations by Completing the Square

The _____(SRP) states that if $x^2 = a$ for $a \geq 0$,
then $x =$ _____.

Examples. $x^2 = 18$ $(x + 2)^2 = 9$ $(5x - 2)^2 = 3$

Is the equation $x^2 + 6x + 9 = 4$ in the correct form to use the SRP?
How can you get it in the correct form?
Solve.

What makes a perfect square trinomial?
The _____ and _____ terms are perfect squares and the middle
term is _____ the product of the numbers being _____ in the first and
last terms.
A perfect square trinomial is of the form $(a + b)^2 =$
or $(a - b)^2 =$

EXAMPLES 1–2 Fill in the blanks to create a perfect square trinomial.
$x^2 + 8x +$ _____ $= (x +$ ____$)^2$

$x^2 - 12x +$ _____ $= (x -$ ____$)^2$

This is called "_____".
Note: To get the constant term of a perfect square trinomial where $a = 1$,
find _____ of the coefficient of ___, and _____ the result.

EXAMPLE 3 Solve $x^2 + 2x = 3$ by filling in the blanks and then using the
Square Root Property.
$x^2 + 2x +$ _____ $= 3 +$ _____

Write the steps for solving a quadratic equation by completing the square.

1. If the coefficient of x^2 is 1, ...
   If not, get the coefficient to 1 by _____ each term of the equation by the _____ of x^2.
2. Write the _____ so that all terms with _____ are on one side of the equation and all _____ are on the other.
3. Find _____ of the _____ of x and then _____ the result. _____ to both sides of the equation.
4. _____ the resulting perfect square trinomial. _____ the other side.
5. Use the _____ to solve the resulting equation.

Note: When might an equation be more easily solved by a different method?

EXAMPLE 4 Solve by completing the square. $x^2 + 4x - 5 = 0$

EXAMPLE 5 Solve by completing the square. $x^2 + 6x + 1 = 0$

CONCEPT CHECK:
What is the first step to solving $2x^2 + 12x = -22$ by completing the square?

GUIDED EXAMPLES:

1. Fill in the blanks to create a perfect square trinomial.
   $$x^2 - 10x + \underline{\quad} = (x - \underline{\quad})^2$$

2. Solve by completing the square.
   $$x^2 + 6x - 7 = 0$$

3. Solve by completing the square.
   $$3x^2 + 12x - 36 = 0$$

4. Solve by completing the square.
   $$2x^2 + 4x + 1 = 0$$

Notebook 32.5
Solving Quadratic Equations Using the Quadratic Formula

OTHER NOTES

State the Quadratic Formula. Remember, this is for all quadratic equations of the form $ax^2 + bx + c = 0$.

Write the steps for solving an equation using the Quadratic Formula.
1. Write the equation in _____ form.
    What does that mean?
2. Identify a, b, and c.
3. Substitute a, b, and c, into the _____,

$$x = \frac{-b \pm \sqrt{b^2 - 4ac}}{2a}.$$

4. _____.

SUMMARY OF SOLVING QUADRATIC EQUATIONS
When might the factoring method be easiest?

When should you consider using the Square Root Property?

When might Completing the Square work nicely?

What is the advantage for using the Quadratic Formula?

EXAMPLE 1 Solve by using the quadratic formula. $3x^2 - x - 2 = 0$
Write in standard form.
Identify a, b, and c.
Substitute.
Simplify.

EXAMPLE 2 Solve by using the quadratic formula. $x^2 = 6x$
Write in standard form.
Identify a, b, and c.
Substitute.
Simplify.

Caution! What will make b or $c = 0$? Is this ok?

EXAMPLE 3 Solve by using the quadratic formula. $4x^2 + 25 = 20x$

Write in standard form.

Identify a, b, and c.

Substitute.

Simplify.

EXAMPLE 4 Solve by using the quadratic formula. $5x^2 - 2x + 3 = 0$

Write in standard form.

Identify a, b, and c.

Substitute.

Simplify.

EXAMPLE 5 Solve by using the quadratic formula. $x^2 + 4x - 8 = 0$

Write in standard form.

Identify a, b, and c.

Substitute.

Simplify.

Caution! Make sure you divide _____ terms in the formula by $2a$.

CONCEPT CHECK:

What are the values of a, b, and c, for the quadratic equation $5x^2 + 2x - 10 = 0$?

GUIDED EXAMPLES:

Solve by using the quadratic formula.

1. $x^2 - 4x + 3 = 0$

2. $x^2 + 5x = -1 + 2x$

3. $2x^2 - 26 = 0$

4. $4x^2 = -4x - 1$

246

Name: _____   Date: _____

Instructor: _____   Section: _____

Review Solving Quadratic Equations

Strategies for Solving a Quadratic Equation
- Factoring
- Completing the Square
- Quadratic Formula

EXAMPLE 1 Solve. $\dfrac{1}{4} + \dfrac{1}{y} = \dfrac{6}{y+6}$

EXAMPLE 2 Solve. $\dfrac{1}{x+2} + \dfrac{1}{x} = \dfrac{1}{8}$

EXAMPLE 3 Solve. $x^4 - 19x^2 + 48 = 0$

The discriminant of a quadratic equation is the number $b^2 - 4ac$. This number can be used to determine how many and what type of solutions the quadratic equation will have.

If the discriminant is:	The equation will have:
Positive and a perfect square	
Positive and not a perfect square	
Zero	
Negative	

EXAMPLE 4 Use the discriminant to determine the type of solutions.

$5x^2 + 3x = 5$

Notebook 33.1
Complex Numbers

What is an imaginary number?

What makes up the set of imaginary numbers?

For all positive real numbers a, $\sqrt{-a} =$

EXAMPLES 1 & 2 Simplify.

$\sqrt{-49}$

$\sqrt{-8}$

Imaginary Numbers:

$i =$ $i^5 =$

$i^2 =$ $i^6 =$

$i^3 =$ $i^7 =$

$i^4 =$ $i^8 =$

Note: $i^{4n} =$ _____ where $n \neq 0$.

EXAMPLES 3 & 4 Evaluate the powers of i.

$i^9 =$

$i^{15} =$

What are complex numbers? Numbers of the form _____, where a and b are _____. The a is the _____ and bi is the

_____.

For all real numbers a, b, c, and d, $(a + bi) + (c + di) =$
and $(a + bi) - (c + di) =$

EXAMPLES 5 & 6 Add or Subtract.

$(5 + 6i) + (6 - 3i)$

$(3.5 + 7i) - (1 + 4i)$

249

Which properties apply to complex numbers as well as real numbers?

EXAMPLE 7 Multiply.
$5i(3 + 2i)$

A complex number can be a _____.
To multiply two binomials, use _____.

EXAMPLES 8 & 9 Multiply.
$(7 - 6i)(2 + 3i)$

$(5 + 3i)(5 - 3i)$

The expressions $(a + b)$ and $(a - b)$ are called _____. The
product of conjugates is always a _____.
Remember, $(a + b)(a - b) =$ _____.

Dividing complex numbers is exactly like _____ the
denominator.

EXAMPLE 10 Divide
$$\frac{7 + i}{3 - 2i}$$

CONCEPT CHECK:
When $(4 - 3i)(1 + 2i)$ is multiplied by FOIL, what will the "L" term simplify to?

GUIDED EXAMPLES:
1. Simplify. $\sqrt{-36}$

2. Evaluate the powers of i. i^{13}

3. Add. $(11 + 2.4i) + (6 + 1.6i)$

4. Multiply. $(3i + 2)(4i + 1)$

Notebook 33.2
The Discriminant in the Quadratic Formula

For all quadratic equations of the form $ax^2 + bx + c = 0$, state the quadratic formula.

_____ can be expressed as a _____ of two integers. When written in decimal form, rational numbers are _____ or _____ decimals.
Examples.

_____ are non-terminating, non-repeating decimals.
Examples.

The _____ i is defined as _____ and _____. The set of imaginary numbers consists of numbers of the form _____, where b is a real number and $b \neq 0$.

_____ are numbers of the form _____, where a is the _____ and bi is the _____.

Observe the following examples and take note of the different types of solutions.

$x^2 - 11x + 28 = 0$ Solutions: Type:

$x^2 + 5x - 12 = 0$ Solutions: Type:

$x^2 - 6x + 9 = 0$ Solutions: Type:

$x^2 + x + 5 = 0$ Solutions: Type

What is the discriminant of a quadratic equation?
What does a discriminant tell us?

If $b^2 - 4ac$ is …	Then there are …

EXAMPLES 1 & 2 Use the discriminant to determine how many and what kind
of solutions the quadratic equations will have. Do not solve the equations.
$5x^2 - 8 = 4$

$9x^2 + 24x + 16 = 0$

EXAMPLES 3 & 4 Use the discriminant to determine how many and what kind of solutions the quadratic equations will have. Do not solve the equations.

$4x^2 + 81 = 0$

$3x^2 + 4x - 2 = 0$

CONCEPT CHECK:

What piece of the quadratic formula will result in the discriminant?

GUIDED EXAMPLES:

1. Use the discriminant to determine the number of and types of solutions to the quadratic equation. Do not solve the equation.

   $6x^2 - 3x + 4 = 0$

2. Use the discriminant to determine the number of and types of solutions to the quadratic equation. Do not solve the equation.

   $2x^2 + 10x + 8 = 0$

3. Use the discriminant to determine the number of and types of solutions to the quadratic equation. Do not solve the equation.

   $\frac{1}{2}x^2 - 2x - \frac{3}{4} = 0$

4. Use the discriminant to determine the number of and types of solutions to the quadratic equation. Then solve the equation.

   $3x^2 - 5 = 7x$

Notebook 33.3
Solving Quadratic Equations with Real or Complex Number Solutions

State the Quadratic Formula. Remember, this is for all quadratic equations of the form $ax^2 + bx + c = 0$, $x =$

The _____ of a quadratic equation is the simplified value of _____.

The discriminant tells the nature of the solutions to a _____ equation.

If $b^2 - 4ac$ is …	Then the solutions will be …
Positive and a perfect square	
Positive, but not a perfect square	
Zero	
negative	

The _____, i, is defined as $i = \sqrt{-1}$ and $i^2 = -1$.

Complex numbers are written in the form _____.

EXAMPLE 1 Solve by using the quadratic formula. $x^2 - 8x + 10 = 0$
Identify a, b, and c.
Substitute.
Simplify.

EXAMPLE 2 Solve by using the quadratic formula. $x^2 - 5x - 24 = 0$
Identify a, b, and c.
Substitute.
Simplify.

EXAMPLE 3 Solve by using the quadratic formula. $x^2 - 2x + 8 = 0$
Identify a, b, and c.
Substitute.
Simplify.

EXAMPLE 4 Solve by using the quadratic formula. $3x^2 + 6 = 4x$

Write in standard form.

Identify a, b, and c.

Substitute.

Simplify.

EXAMPLE 5 Solve by using the quadratic formula. $8x^2 - 4x + 1 = 0$

Identify a, b, and c.

Substitute.

Simplify.

CONCEPT CHECK:

Identify a, b, and c for the equation $3x^2 = -2x + 1$.

GUIDED EXAMPLES:

1. Solve by using the quadratic formula. $5x^2 - 12x + 7 = 0$

2. Solve by using the quadratic formula. $3x^2 + 8x + 1 = 0$

3. Solve by using the quadratic formula. $5x^2 + 9 = 6x$

4. Solve by using the quadratic formula. $2x(x + 2) + 11 = 6$

254

Notebook 34.1
Introduction to Graphing Quadratic Functions

A _____ is an equation that may be written in the form $ax^2 + bx + c = 0$, where $a \neq 0$.

Sketch the graph of $y = x^2$.

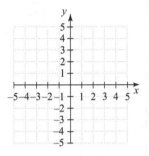

What is the vertex of a parabola?

What is the axis of symmetry of a parabola?

How do you determine if the parabola opens upward or downward?

How does that affect the vertex?

EXAMPLES 1–3 Determine whether the graph of each quadratic equation opens upward or downward.

$y = 2x^2 - 6x + 3$

$y = -5x^2 + 11$

$y = -x^2 + 4x - 1$

EXAMPLES 4–6 If an item is dropped from a height of 400 feet, its height above the ground t seconds after being dropped is given by the equation $h = -16t^2 + 400$. Determine the height of the object for the following values of t.

0 seconds

1 second

5 seconds

CONCEPT CHECK:

What is the vertex of a parabola?

GUIDED EXAMPLES:

1. Determine whether the graph of each quadratic equation opens upward or downward.

    $y = -2x^2 + x + 5$

2. Determine whether the graph of each quadratic equation opens upward or downward.

    $y = x^2 - 1$

3. If a football player kicks a field goal with an initial vertical velocity of 50 feet/second, its height above the ground t seconds after being kicked is given by the equation $s = -16t^2 + 50t$. Determine the height of the football for the following value of t. 2 seconds

4. If a football player kicks a field goal with an initial vertical velocity of 50 feet/second, its height above the ground t seconds after being kicked is given by the equation $s = -16t^2 + 50t$. Determine the height of the football for the following value of t. 3 seconds

Notebook 34.2
Finding the Vertex of a Quadratic Function

A _____ is an equation that may be written in the form $ax^2 + bx + c = 0$, where $a \neq 0$.

What is the vertex of a parabola?

When will the parabola open upward?
Where is the vertex located?

When will the parabola open downward?
Where is the vertex located?

Sketch the graphs of each of these situations.
$$a > 0 \qquad\qquad\qquad\qquad a < 0$$

Write the steps for finding the vertex of a quadratic equation.
1.

2.

3.

Note: Which variable determines if the parabola opens upward or downward?
Explain this.

EXAMPLE 1 Find the vertex of the quadratic equation. Is the vertex a maximum or a minimum? $y = x^2 - 8x + 15$

Identify a, b, and c.
Find x.
Substitute to find y.
Determine if vertex is a maximum or a minimum.

EXAMPLE 2 Find the vertex of the quadratic equation. Is the vertex a maximum or a minimum? $y = 12x - 3x^2 - 6$

257

EXAMPLE 3 Find the vertex of the quadratic equation. Is the vertex a maximum or a minimum? $y = 5x^2 - 7$

CONCEPT CHECK:

What is the formula for finding the x-coordinate of the vertex for $y = 2x^2 + 20x - 1$?

GUIDED EXAMPLES:

1. Find the vertex of the quadratic equation. Is the vertex a maximum or a minimum?

   $y = x^2 - 6x + 5$

2. Find the vertex of the quadratic equation. Is the vertex a maximum or a minimum?

   $y = 3x^2 + 12x + 7$

3. Find the vertex of the quadratic equation. Is the vertex a maximum or a minimum?

   $y = -4x^2 - 2x + 1$

4. Find the vertex of the quadratic equation. Is the vertex a maximum or a minimum?

   $y = -2x^2 + 10$

258

Name: _____   Date: _____

Instructor: _____   Section: _____

Notebook 34.3
Finding the Intercepts of a Quadratic Function

The point on the graph where a line or curve crosses an axis is called an

_____.

What is the point on the graph where the curve crosses the x-axis?
What is the ordered pair that represents that point?

How do you find any x-intercepts?

What is the point on the graph where the curve crosses the y-axis?
What ordered pair represents that point?

How do you find any y-intercepts?

How many x-intercepts will a quadratic function have?

How many y-intercepts will a quadratic function have?

Sketch the graphs that demonstrate this. Explain.

How do you find the y-intercept of a quadratic function?

EXAMPLES 1 & 2 Find the y-intercept of each quadratic function.
$f(x) = x^2 + 6x + 15$

$f(x) = 3x^2$

How do you find the x-intercept(s) of a quadratic function?

EXAMPLES 3 & 4 Find the x-intercept(s) of each quadratic function, if any exist.

$f(x) = x^2 + 2x - 24$

$f(x) = x^2 + 1$

EXAMPLE 5 Find the x- and y-intercepts of the quadratic function.

$f(x) = x^2 + 5x - 14$

Find the x-intercepts.

Find the y-intercepts.

CONCEPT CHECK:

How is the y-intercept of a quadratic function found?

GUIDED EXAMPLES:

1. Find the y-intercept of the quadratic function. $f(x) = x^2 + 3x - 10$

2. Find the y-intercept of the quadratic function. $f(x) = -2x^2 + 4x - 5$

3. Find the x-intercept(s) of the quadratic function, if any exist.

   $f(x) = x^2 + 17$

4. Find the x-intercept(s) of the quadratic function, if any exist.

   $f(x) = 5x^2 + 3x$

260

Name: _____   Date: _____

Instructor: _____   Section: _____

Notebook 34.4
Graphing Quadratic Functions Summary

The graph of a quadratic equation $y = ax^2 + bx + c$ is a _____.

The highest or lowest point on a parabola is the _____.
If $a > 0$, then …

If $a < 0$, then …

Where is the vertex of a parabola located?

The point where the curve crosses the x-axis is the _____.
How do you find the x-intercept(s)?

The point where the curve crosses the y-axis is the _____.
How do you find the y-intercept?

What is the axis of symmetry?

What does it mean to be symmetric?

What is the equation for an axis of symmetry?

EXAMPLE 1 Graph the equation.
$y = x^2$

x	y

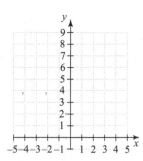

Write the steps for graphing a quadratic equation.
1. Determine the _____ of the parabola.
2. Find the _____ of the equation.
3. Find the _____ of the equation.
4. If no x-intercepts, find _____.
5. Plot the _____, _____ and _____.
6. Draw a _____ through the points.

EXAMPLE 2 Graph the equation.

$y = x^2 - 6x + 8$

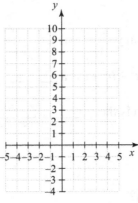

EXAMPLE 3 Graph the equation.

$y = -2x^2 + 4x - 3$

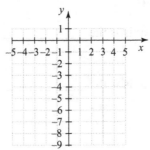

CONCEPT CHECK:

What does the equation of the axis of symmetry look like for a parabola of the form $y = ax^2 + bx + c$?

GUIDED EXAMPLES: Graph the equations.

1. $y = x^2 - 6x + 5$

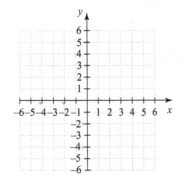

2. $y = -2x^2 - 8x - 6$

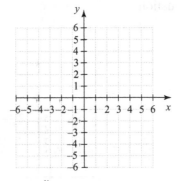

3. $y = -x^2 + 2x - 2$

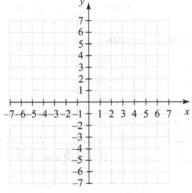

262

Name: _____   Date: _____

Instructor: _____   Section: _____

Notebook 35.1
Interval Notation

What symbol represents each of the following phrases?
"is less than"
"is less than or equal to"
"is greater than"
"is greater than or equal to"

What does an open circle show on a graph?
What does a closed circle show on a graph?

What does the graph of an inequality represent?
How do you graph linear inequalities?

Example.
$x > 3$

_____ is another way to represent the solution to an
inequality.
What two values does interval notation use?

Note: When do you use a parenthesis in interval notation and when do you use
a bracket?

Example.

Caution! Interval notation is not the same as an _____!

An _____ is a set whose elements cannot be counted.

What is infinity?

What is negative infinity?

When an interval contains all the points to ∞ or $-\infty$, you must use it as one
of the _____. These symbols get _____ in interval
notation.

Example. $x > 3$

263

EXAMPLES 1 & 2 Graph each inequality and write in interval notation.

$x < -2$

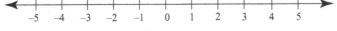

$x \geq 0$

Inequality	Graph	Interval Notation
$x > a$		
$x \geq a$		
$x < a$		
$x \leq a$		

Note: A parentheses is always used to enclose _____ and _____.

Inequality	Graph	Interval Notation
$a < x < b$		
$a \leq x \leq b$		
$a \leq x < b$		
$a < x \leq b$		

EXAMPLES 3–6 Graph each inequality and write in interval notation.

$-1 \leq x < 4$ $\qquad\qquad\qquad\qquad$ $-3 \leq x \leq 0$

$-2 < x < 2$ $\qquad\qquad\qquad\qquad$ $-1.5 < x \leq 3$

CONCEPT CHECK:

Describe the graph of $(-\infty, 3]$.

GUIDED EXAMPLES: Graph each inequality and write the interval notation.

1. $n \leq 0$

2. $x < -1.5$

3. $1 < x \leq 3.5$

4. $-8 \leq x < -4.1$

264

Notebook 35.2
Graphing Compound Inequalities

What is the difference between an "and" statement and an "or" statement?

$x > -2$

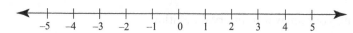

$x \leq 4$

EXAMPLE 1 Graph. Write your answer in interval notation.

$x > -2$ and $x \leq 4$

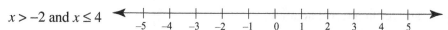

What is a compound inequality?

Write the steps for graphing a compound inequality.
1. _____ the first inequality.
    a.
    b.
    c.
2. _____ the second inequality.
3. Graph the _____ to the _____.

Note: Where do you shade for "and" and where do you shade for "or"?

What are some different ways to write "and" inequalities?

EXAMPLES 2–4 Graph.

$-3 \leq x < 3$

$(-2, 5]$

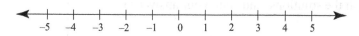

$x > 4$ and $x < 1$

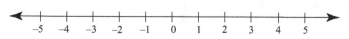

265

EXAMPLE 5 The U.S. Air Force requires female pilots to be at least 58 inches tall, but they cannot be more than 80 inches tall. Write a compound inequality in set notation and in interval notation. Then graph the solutions.

EXAMPLES 6 & 7 Graph. Write your answer in interval notation.

$x > 3$ or $x \le -2$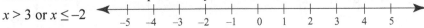

$x \ge -1$ or $x \le 5$

EXAMPLE 8 Graph. Write your answer in interval notation.

$n < 4$ and $n < -2$

EXAMPLE 9 Graph. Write your answer in interval notation.

$x < 5$ or $x < -3$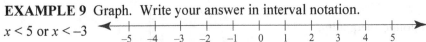

CONCEPT CHECK:

A talent show states that the contestants must be at least 16 years of age, but no greater than 28 years of age. How will this be written as an inequality?

GUIDED EXAMPLES:

Graph. Write your answer in interval notation.

1. $y \ge -2$ and $y \le 1$

2. $x > 1$ and $x \le 5$

3. To ride a roller coaster, riders are required to be at least 44 inches tall, but they cannot be more than 81 inches tall. Write a compound inequality to represent this situation. Graph the solutions, and state your answer in interval notation.

4. Graph. Write your answer in interval notation.

   $x > 1$ or $x \le -1$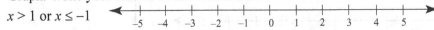

Notebook 35.3
Solving Compound Inequalities

Graph.

$x > -2$ and $x \leq 3$

EXAMPLE 1 Solve and graph. Then write your answer in interval notation.

$x + 1 > -2$ and $x - 2 \leq 2$

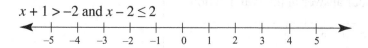

EXAMPLE 2 Solve and graph. Then write your answer in interval notation.

$3x + 2 \geq 14$ or $2x - 1 \leq -7$

Solve and graph the first inequality.
Solve and graph the second inequality.
Graph the solution to the compound inequality.
Write in interval notation.

EXAMPLE 3 Solve and graph. Then write your answer in interval notation.

$3x + 5 \leq 17$ or $-4x > 12$

Solve and graph the first inequality.
Solve and graph the second inequality.
Graph the solution to the compound inequality.
Write in interval notation.

267

EXAMPLE 4 Solve and graph. Then write your answer in interval notation.

$6 + x < 9$ or $5x + 2 > -18$

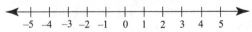

Solve and graph the first inequality.
Solve and graph the second inequality.
Graph the solution to the compound inequality.
Write in interval notation.

EXAMPLE 5 Solve and graph. Then write your answer in interval notation.

$-9 \leq 3a - 3 < 9$

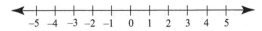

Solve and graph the first inequality.
Solve and graph the second inequality.
Graph the solution to the compound inequality.
Write in interval notation.

EXAMPLE 6 Solve and graph. Then write your answer in interval notation.

$12 < -2x + 3 < 1$

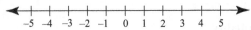

Solve the first inequality.
Solve the second inequality.

CONCEPT CHECK:
How would the solution to the compound inequality "$x + 1 > 3$ and $2x \leq 8$" be written in interval notation?

GUIDED EXAMPLES: Solve and graph. Then write the solution in interval notation.

1. $2x + 3 \leq 5$ and $-x - 1 \leq 2$

2. $2n + 3 > -7$ or $7n - 1 > 13$

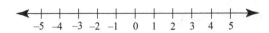

3. $3x + 9 > -6$ or $7x + 6 \leq 20$

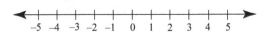

4. $-40 \leq 8m - 16 \leq -8$

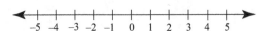

268

Notebook 36.1
Introduction to Absolute Value Equations

OTHER NOTES

The _____ of a number is the distance between
that number and zero on a number line.

EXAMPLE 1 Solve. $|x| = 2$

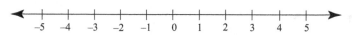

EXAMPLES 2–4 Solve.
$|x| = 8.35$

$|y| = 0$

$|x| = -11$

EXAMPLE 5 Solve. $|x| + 1 = 10$

EXAMPLE 6 Solve. $-6|x| = -72$

EXAMPLES 7 & 8 Write an equation using absolute value to represent the given graph.

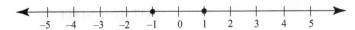

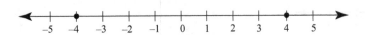

CONCEPT CHECK:

What is the FIRST step to solving $2|x| - 3 = -2$?

GUIDED EXAMPLES: See guided examples

1. Solve. $|y| = 7$

2. Isolate the absolute value, then solve. $|a| - 18 = -6$

3. Isolate the absolute value, then solve. $-3|x| = -5.4$

4. Write an equation using absolute value to represent the given graph.

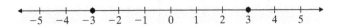

270

Name: _____   Date: _____

Instructor: _____   Section: _____

Notebook 36.2
Solving Basic Absolute Value Equations

If $|x| = a$, and a is a positive real number, then _____.
The _____ of a number is the _____
between that number and _____ on a number line.

Example. If $|x| = 4$, then $x = 4$ or $x = -4$.

Write the steps for solving absolute value equations.
1.

2.

3.

EXAMPLE 1 Solve. $|x + 1| = 6$
Write as two separate equations.

Solve the resulting equations.

Check.

EXAMPLE 2 Solve. $|5y| = 35$

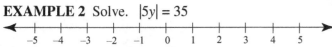

Write as two separate equations.

Solve the resulting equations.

Check.

EXAMPLE 3 Solve. $\left|\dfrac{1}{2}x - 1\right| = 5$

271

EXAMPLES 4 Solve. $|3x - 1| + 2 = 5$

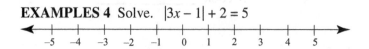

Isolate the absolute value.

Write as two equations.

Solve.

Check.

EXAMPLE 5 Solve. $|8x - 3| + 12 = 7$

Caution! An absolution value can never equal a _____!

CONCEPT CHECK:
What are the two equations that will be solved for $|2x + 6| = 10$?

GUIDED EXAMPLES: Solve.

1. $|x + 5| = 17$

2. $|7x - 3| = 11$

3. $\left| \dfrac{1}{2} - \dfrac{3}{4}x \right| = 2$

4. $|2x + 1| - 3 = 2$

272

Name: _____   Date: _____

Instructor: _____   Section: _____

Notebook 36.4
Solving Absolute Value Inequalities

Consider $|x| < 4$.

What does it mean if $|x| < a$?
In interval notation, if $|x| < a$, then …

Consider $|x| > 4$.

What does it mean if $|x| > a$?
In interval notation, if $|x| > a$, then …

EXAMPLES 1 & 2 Graph. Write the answer in interval notation.

$|x| \geq 2$

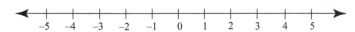

$|x| < 3$

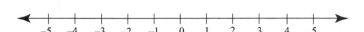

How do you know when to use parentheses or brackets?

EXAMPLE 3 Solve and graph. Write the answer in interval notation.
$|x + 5| \leq 10$
Rewrite according to appropriate rule.
Solve.
Graph and write interval notation.

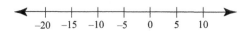

EXAMPLE 4 Solve and graph. Write the answer in interval notation.

$|-2x - 1| \geq 7$

$$\begin{array}{c} \xleftarrow{\hspace{0.3cm}} \begin{array}{cccccccccccc} | & | & | & | & | & | & | & | & | & | & | \\ -5 & -4 & -3 & -2 & -1 & 0 & 1 & 2 & 3 & 4 & 5 \end{array} \xrightarrow{\hspace{0.3cm}} \end{array}$$

EXAMPLE 5 Solve and graph. Write the answer in interval notation.

$|4x + 2| + 5 > 9$

Isolate the absolute value.

Rewrite according to appropriate rule.

Solve.

Graph and write interval notation.

EXAMPLE 6 Solve and graph. Write the answer in interval notation.

$|x| > -2$

$$\begin{array}{c} \xleftarrow{\hspace{0.3cm}} \begin{array}{cccccccccccc} | & | & | & | & | & | & | & | & | & | & | \\ -5 & -4 & -3 & -2 & -1 & 0 & 1 & 2 & 3 & 4 & 5 \end{array} \xrightarrow{\hspace{0.3cm}} \end{array}$$

The solution set is _____.

EXAMPLE 7 Solve and graph. Write the answer in interval notation.

$|x| \leq -6$

$$\begin{array}{c} \xleftarrow{\hspace{0.3cm}} \begin{array}{cccccccccccc} | & | & | & | & | & | & | & | & | & | & | \\ -5 & -4 & -3 & -2 & -1 & 0 & 1 & 2 & 3 & 4 & 5 \end{array} \xrightarrow{\hspace{0.3cm}} \end{array}$$

This inequality has _____.

CONCEPT CHECK:

What is the interval notation for $|x| \geq 3$?

GUIDED EXAMPLES:

1. Graph on a number line. $|x| \geq 4$

$$\begin{array}{c} \xleftarrow{\hspace{0.3cm}} \begin{array}{cccccccccccc} | & | & | & | & | & | & | & | & | & | & | \\ -5 & -4 & -3 & -2 & -1 & 0 & 1 & 2 & 3 & 4 & 5 \end{array} \xrightarrow{\hspace{0.3cm}} \end{array}$$

2. Solve and graph. Write the solution in interval notation. $|x + 3| \leq 7$

$$\begin{array}{c} \xleftarrow{\hspace{0.3cm}} \begin{array}{cccccccccccc} | & | & | & | & | & | & | & | & | & | & | \\ -5 & -4 & -3 & -2 & -1 & 0 & 1 & 2 & 3 & 4 & 5 \end{array} \xrightarrow{\hspace{0.3cm}} \end{array}$$

3. Solve and graph. Write the solution in interval notation. $|4x - 3| < 9$

$$\begin{array}{c} \xleftarrow{\hspace{0.3cm}} \begin{array}{cccccccccccc} | & | & | & | & | & | & | & | & | & | & | \\ -5 & -4 & -3 & -2 & -1 & 0 & 1 & 2 & 3 & 4 & 5 \end{array} \xrightarrow{\hspace{0.3cm}} \end{array}$$

4. Solve and graph. $|3x + 5| + 9 \geq 26$

$$\begin{array}{c} \xleftarrow{\hspace{0.3cm}} \begin{array}{cccccccccccc} | & | & | & | & | & | & | & | & | & | & | \\ -5 & -4 & -3 & -2 & -1 & 0 & 1 & 2 & 3 & 4 & 5 \end{array} \xrightarrow{\hspace{0.3cm}} \end{array}$$